CONAMARA MAN

CONAMARA MAN

※

Seamus Ridge

PRENTICE-HALL, INC., ENGLEWOOD CLIFFS, NEW JERSEY

CONAMARA MAN by Seamus Ridge

© 1969 by Irene Ridge

Copyright under International and Pan American
Copyright Conventions

Library of Congress Catalog Card Number: 69–12839

Printed in the United States of America · T

Prentice-Hall International, Inc., London
Prentice-Hall of Australia, Pty. Ltd., Sydney
Prentice-Hall of Canada, Ltd., Toronto
Prentice-Hall of India Private Ltd., New Delhi
Prentice-Hall of Japan, Inc., Tokyo

For
IRENE

CONAMARA MAN

I do often wonder why I came here. Ach musha,* but there is a world of difference between this big city and Muighinis,† the island in Conamara where I was born and where the material wants so necessary to the New Yorker are lacking, but where the fresh air, freedom of the sea, and enjoyment of life is as God meant it to be. Old Paudeen used to say: "Look at the stingy thin and wrinkled face of the returned Yank and learn a lesson from it."

Yet, it did seem to myself that there was something noble about going far away. Indeed, I thought it would be wonderful to visit the different countries and find out about the culture and customs of life practiced by the natives. I did love my own land, and any time I ever had left it was just like tearing a part of myself away and happy was I finding myself home again and fishing on the sea. But so contrary is a human being that as soon as I felt at my ease again, the lust for traveling would take a strong hold of me.

Even now, though a half century has passed since I left my island home, the picture etched in my mind is clear galore: the rugged grandeur of the Bens of Beola, their heathery cheeks, the bewitching beauty of shore and sea that were all around me.

The name Muighinis means island plain in the English, and it suits well enough too, for a part of the island is a plain or sandy beach. Yet, other parts are craggy, with

* *Ach musha:* Dear me
† *Muighinis:* pronounced Mweenish

heights and hollows, steep cliffs and piles of granite boulders scattered here and there.

Wild, exposed and rocky the south and west shores are. Where the land was soft, the restless sea in her hours of madness devoured it gradually night and day down through the ages so that she might thrust her arms further into the land. To spite that, however, the land pushed out its hard bare teeth of granite, defying the angry breakers. And those inlets of the sea serve a useful purpose as natural harbors: narrow at the entrance, deep and sheltered inside, with natural steps here and there in the rocks for easy landing places.

The north and east shores are more serene—sheltered by the rising ground from the fury of the broad Atlantic and the storms from the southwest. The eighty homes are built along by the shore, for the islanders earn their living from the sea. This fishing and kelp-making is a hard livelihood. Early and late they needs must be out on the big sea: betimes alas! with their feet right on the edge of a watery grave.

As for land, it is little they have of it: small gardens full of rocks and the soil in many places not a foot deep. If favorable be the year, the potatoes and corn grew plentifully. Or, as the Conamara man says, "March dry and windy, soft dew in April, sunshine and showers in May and a sunny mild autumn."

Those small gardens were flat rocks many years ago. It was our forefathers who by their skill and perseverance made them into what they are today. With much hard work they coped with the unruly elements down through the ages: building strong walls around these rocky patches, breaking stones and packing them into the clefts. They carried sand, shells and weed from the shore on their backs, climbing up the cliffs and spilling basket after basket on the bare granite, mixing in a little clay that they had picked out of slits. But when the Islander had a garden created by his industry, it put high gladness in his heart, and the hard work he had done was well rewarded at harvest time.

In the summer when the sea around is calm and smooth, my Island is a lovely place. The fine white sand dazzling under the rays of the sun. Patches of rye and potatoes mantled with thick foliage. To the east of our cottage a fine stretch of level green reaches down toward the sea. On this grassy bawn, one notices hundreds of tiny buttercups, primroses, daisies and bluebells, each not much bigger than a pin's point. Clover plants and shamrocks highlight the emerald sward on the rim of the sea, all woven through the short grass-like threads of many colors.

In a small glen nearby where the golden-blossomed iris grew, also is found that devilish flytrap called, in the Gaelic, Trop-na-gcuileog. This seven-inch plant opens out its reddish-brown petals at sunrise with what looks like drops of honey glistening on the leaves set to lure the unwary fly. The silly insect alights softly to have a meal, but the petals fold swiftly to imprison the invader. When the trapper has his hunger satisfied, the leaves spread out again and a puff of wind blows away the residue of that one who had wished to dine first.

Birds in a merry mood from the pleasant warmth flit and coo in the blackberry bushes. Wrens build their nests in the green ivy that clings to the face of the tall cliff. The lark with her trilling sweet melody soars on high in the clear blue heavens. Snowy gulls and terns wheel overhead, black cormorants doze on the rocks and sandpipers rush here and there looking for a mouthful. Peace and quiet are all around, as some folks stretch on the strand and others swim in the placid water.

"Cuckoo, cuckoo." All would look and listen. If the old man hears her call from the patch of the graveyard, a queer feeling comes over him. Old Crossbones himself would surely pick him up ere that time again. But the colleen would be happy, as it would be a promise true by the cuckoo that her lover would come from that direction within the year.

When the dreary winter sets in, the picture is much different. Blustering westerlies and southerlies rush from the bosom of the big sea in fearful gales, giving the Conamara Islands a weird and gloomy look. Sea waves, mountain high, driven by the storm, hurl themselves with foaming manes, hiss and keen against the granite shore. The surfbeat on Long Strand is loud and continuous. Big blobs of white foam are blown around to find shelter in the lee of the dark cliffs. The Atlantic away to the west is like frothing milk, and the cheeks of the Beola Hills are mantled with the fresh snow.

Often in rough weather ominous clouds move in toward the land. Vivid flashes of lightning flicker on their dark faces. Sharp hailstones, each one as big as a pullet's egg, fall for a few moments, charging the air with the smell of sulphur. Then—a flash of lightning bluer than indigo is followed by a loud thunderclap, as if all the smooth oval stones lying on the beach are spilled all at once from the heavens above.

The ebb and flow of the tide is the shoredweller's life pulse, his hope from the cradle to the grave. Even the cradle itself—the coffin that he is laid to rest in on the last day—might have come in with the tide. On finding a fine pine or mahogany plank, the Islander puts it away for the day that makes no lie. Val Mor himself, though still young in years, had four white pine boards seasoning for seven years in the loft. But then the bad wet year came when the turf did not dry, and though it went to his heart he needs must burn them to cook a mouthful. Yet, in the end he did not need them. Fate had willed otherwise, and poor Val was drowned one stormy night while out in his pucan* with his nets. His body was never found.

But to do battle with this worthy foe was noble, and early and late the Islander must be out on the sea filling his lungs with the fresh salty air wafted in from the ocean. If the weather be fine and fair in the month of May, I would be one of those fishing along the coast for the basking shark. We would sail our pucans far out to sea, always to the west until the Bens would be sunk under the horizon to the east and the Island of Aranmore itself lay just like a spindle on the surface. The skipper took care to put his mark on the rope buoy, as well as on the harpoon. When a boat neared the shark, the harpooner aimed at a white spot near the back fin where the iron went in easy. Sometimes if the pucan could come close enough to the beast, the clever harpooner had only to rub the ticklish white spot with the point of his harpoon. The shark, enjoying this, pressed up against the point until the fisherman with a quick thrust plunged his weapon in to the hilt.

Many strange sights the fisherman notices out on the big sea, yet he has only to step outside the door and see the mirage at the dawn of day: wild rocks changing into castles, ships and forests. When evening comes, he can see the boats sailing out in the distance to the fishing bank to shoot their nets and trap the schools of mackerel; the soft

* *pucan:* boat with one sail

brown sails of the Nobbies—Conamara Lass, Colleen Bawn, Shamrock, Fagabealach—belly out with the light southerly. The big sun sinking in the west bathes the Bens of Beola in a flood of gold. Tramore, with the wavelets breaking in on the smooth silvery sand and the glossy laminaria* left behind by the ebbing tide, glows bright with the phosphorescence. Low resonant voices are heard spinning the old stories or singing the Gaelic songs or humming lullabies.

* *laminaria:* red weed

*

I must say now that I have spent the best and happiest years of my life with the Islanders. Those of them who have found death, may the blessings of dear God be with their souls—Arrah, who says that they are dead at all? Indeed, they are not dead to me as I can still see them and hear their voices. Daida steering the pucan with his blue knitted gansey on and his fair hair blowing in the wind. Now and again he glances under the apron of the mainsail to find out if he can draw the Point under on his lee without having to come about on another tack. Myself and Kieran along with him. My own thoughts wandering to the greatness in the life of the sailor and myself imagining to be one—maybe a mate or even a captain—painting fancy pictures of me steering a full-rigged vessel along the shore of Muighinis and into Galway docks.

"What about going ashore to cook a mouthful?" Daida would ask at noon, breaking the thread of my thoughts and we fishing for wrasse on the Big Breaker.

We rowed into a horseshoe cove on the north side of Carriagemackan. After tying up the boat, Kieran looked for driftwood to make a fire. Daida cleaned and prepared a fish to cook. I carried the potatoes, milk and a keg of fresh water from the boat to a flat rock on top of this barren reef.

Kieran returned from the west with an armful of driftwood, and carrying his blue beret in the other hand he asked:

"Guess what have I in the cap?"

"Dulse," * I said.

"No-o-o-o! Six fine speckled eggs which I found in the nest of a seabird, and they are all fresh," Kieran beamed. " 'Tis time now to make the fire," throwing down the driftwood.

I started to break up the wood. There were pieces of ships' cabins painted in many colors, splinters of decks from vessels wrecked in the faraway lanes of the Seven Seas. Boards from tea chests that came out of China, old wine-pipe staves from Spain or Portugal, bits of sandal-wood, logwood, rosewood, teak and mahogany which I broke so gently while meditating on their past history and the wide oceans over which they had drifted. When I applied a match to the heap, tongues of flame leaped up interwoven with all the colors of the rainbow, caused, no doubt, by the brass and copper nails, hinges, varnishes and paints on the various kinds of wood. Quaint smells arose from the fire, giving a touch of mystery to our meal on that wild rock many miles west in the Atlantic.

The potatoes roasted in their jackets; the tasty fresh fish browned by the red; the eggs, tea and bread were delicious. After finishing the meal, we stretched out on the smooth rocks in the pleasant warmth of the sun with the air full of fragrance. The sky above was a pale blue marred here and there with tiny specks of sheep shearings. Aranmore to the south lay faintly visible on the horizon from a bluish haze like a huge spider's web with meshes of color. There was soothing peace all around; even the gulls and terns were dozing on the smooth dark flag-stones.

Daida's sweet tenor voice broke the silence with an old Gaelic song:

* *dulse:* edible seaweed

Fain would I ride with thee,
Eileen Aroon.
Fain would I ride with thee,
Eileen Aroon.
Fain would I ride with thee,
To Tirawley's tide with thee,
In hopes to abide with thee,
Eileen Aroon!

We made for the boat and pushed her out with the pole. When clear of the rocks, we put out the oars and headed for the bank. Roving wisps of wind rippled the surface, and the pollacks were in a biting mood. On the first few tacks on the bank we boarded forty fine pollacks. Though we had no desire to leave them, yet it was growing late and we pulled in our lines.

We needs must head for home. The light westerly was in our favor, and it did not take us long to sail the six miles to Muighinis Point. As we walked up the slope from the pier, each of us carrying a basket of cod, pollack and wrasse, the sun was going down in the western sea. The kelp-makers were singing Gaelic songs strolling home from the strand. "Cuckoo, cuckoo, cuckoo" from herself as she perched on the gable end of O'Cooney's before retiring. The green foliage of the potato patch on the side of the bohreen* was folding up for the night. The oil lamp on the wall was lit when we walked in. The catch had to be opened, cleaned and salted down in a barrel. It was late when the supper was finished, the dishes washed and the Rosary said. We needs must be up with the chirp of the sparrow on the morrow, for the first part of the day is the best at the foot of the Breaker.

* *bohreen:* little road or lane

Even when a small lad, I loved to go swinging back and forth on the halyards of the boats alongside the pier and climb up to the top of the masts. Mama did not like me to go near the sea, and used to whisper in my ear now and again: "There's a big black eel out at the end of the pier watching a chance to snatch you away from me."

"Is she as big as this?" I'd ask, stretching out my arms and wonder in my eyes.

"Much bigger, a stór," * she'd reply, holding me in her arms and kissing me.

When Kieran and I had grown old enough to join Daida, I would rise up early each morning to push the boat out of the pier so that she would be afloat later on. Going east to the shore, I could see in the dim light the blackthorn bushes at the side of the bohreen covered with a thin gossamer of bright webbing. How the busy spiders must have weaved during the night, I would think.

Reaching the pier on this morning, I noticed that a good stretch had ebbed and the boat was dry.

"Did you shove her down, Jimeen?" asked Daida, when I returned.

"She was fast aground," I sputtered breathlessly.

"Then, there is no good face on the sea this morning, so be off with you."

And with that I would be gone in a flash to the south shore to search for what the sea had brought in. I had to stoop walking west against the wind which came in sudden gusts. Before long, I found a ship's hatch. Grabbing the iron ring, I dragged it up beyond the high-water mark. On reaching the Point in the west of the village, I stood on a dune and peered out at the Atlantic. An object rose on the crest of a wave. I glued my eye to the spot lest it van-

* *a stór:* treasure

ish like the leprechaun in the old story. Ah, there it was again perched on the comb of the swell and the gale pushing it in towards the land.

"It might come ashore down here in the cove," I said to myself. But just then the undertow coaxed it out again past a reef to the east. As I was trying to decide whether to swim out and secure it, I saw Seaneen Mickil and Paddy son-of-Colm hurrying toward me from the east.

"What do you think it is?" they asked as with one voice.

"It might be a barrel of palm oil and I have in mind to swim out," I answered, running to the mouth of the sea and stopping short where the breakers crashed woolywhite on the dark mussel-coated rocks. The barrel was caught in a crosscurrent moving in when a heavy sea smoking from the crest left it high and dry on the top of a rock where it teetered for a moment and fell with a splash to drift in the shelter of the cliffs.

"What will we do now?" shouted Seaneen, above the roar of the sea.

"I'll swim out," said I, taking off my boots and jumping in.

"May God bless you. Careful now, Jimeen, a little to this side, there—there—" came advice from the pair who were out to their necks and tilting their heads this way and that. When I had left the shelter of the cliff, a comber came roaring after me, so I had to let go of the barrel and dive under. At long last a wave rolled the barrel and myself up on the shore and was about to suck it out again, but my comrades and I clung grimly to the prize and won out.

"Liquor is in it," cried Seaneen, excitedly.

"I'll run up to the house for help," said I, racing up the shore.

"There is a barrel of rum down on the south shore," I gasped, as I came in the door.

Then there was the hurry to find pails and borers. It did not take us long to reach the puncheon and the title printed on its face: *One hundred and sixteen gallons. Made in Jamaica 1916.* The sun came out from behind ragged clouds and we rolling up the barrel. No time was wasted in useless talk. From time to time, one might whisper, "A little bit to this side—careful." At last the rollers took the curves out of their backs, wiped the sweat off their faces with their sleeves and looked at each other.

"Give it the borer," ordered Luke son-of-Paudeen. Intent faces relaxed, and happiness beamed in every eye watching the dark liquor gurgling into the pail.

"Ah, friends of my heart," smiled the Rover, licking his lips. "We can't drink this like poteen,* for like everything else there is a knack in drinking."

"We should thank God and have a holiday in His honor," said Mickileen Liam, in a soft tone. "My soul from the devil, but the Germans have done their share in helping the poor, sick and aged, causing this rum and other good things to come to us."

The news spread until it reached the mainland that galore barrels of rum had come ashore on the Island. When the peelers† heard about it they marched in right away.

"Who was bold enough to open this barrel and steal His Majesty's rum?" the red-haired sergeant shouted, running to the puncheon and slicing a chip from a stave with his knife and putting it in an inside pocket. "We have possession in the name of the Crown now."

* *poteen:* illegally distilled whiskey of Ireland
† *peelers:* English militia

"What did ye come here for?" demanded the Rover, stepping right up to the peelers.

Mickileen Liam reached for a stone. The villagers caught the signal and prepared for a fight. The peelers readied their guns and turned on the Islanders, who stood firm with faces aglow, their pockets full of granite, ready for the fray.

Luke walked over to the barrel, raised his arm in the air and said smilingly, "Wet your lips friends and pay no heed to those tight black pants."

"Ye'll be sorry for this act. Go home now before it is too late and we'll take care of the barrel," advised the sergeant, taking off his helmet and brushing back his thick red hair with the palm of his hand.

"What right has any King to this puncheon or to anything else the generous tide brings in?" shouted Mickileen, leaning on the barrel like the picture on the bottle of rum in the pubs.

"Those robbers are well-paid out of our taxes for telling us that the King of England keeps us alive," Daida added.

"Don't let the liquor astray, Luke," cautioned Mickileen, for the latter was using his finger now instead of the plug.

"Is it not the King's rum?" shifting his finger around searching for the hole.

Seamus son-of-Nora put the flute to his lips. In a short time a set of dancers on a flat rock were keeping time to a jig. While the lads were swinging the girls around, the peelers were gazing out to sea. The player stepped over to the barrel to wet the mouth of his instrument as well as his own. He looked the peelers up and down and started to sing:

Oh, the French are in the bay and they'll be here
Without delay, says the Sean Bhean Bhocht.

"How dare you sing that seditious song?" roared the sergeant.

"The curse of God on you," replied Seamus, taking a step forward.

The sergeant's face turned crimson. "If you come another step nearer—pass that stone now," pointing with his gun.

"I will," replied Seamus.

"You——"

"I'm past it now," taunted Seamus.

"Keep out. If you come any nearer——"

"A long near on you, tight pants," cried Seamus, rushing in and grabbing the gun. The two had each other in a vice-like grip.

"God be with you. Knock him on the rod of his back with the foot-twist," shouted Luke.

The five peelers were giving words of praise to their man. The bawneen* clad peasants were lined around, those in the rear craning their necks trying to see over the heads of those in front. Excitement was high as Seamus pulled the sergeant toward him, bringing him to his knees. The Changeling made his way in through the crowd with dry sand in the corner of his bawneen, which he shook under the feet of the wrestlers. The limb of the law was finding the upper hand in the next round, twisting his rival around at a fast pace, their hobnailed boots taking sparks out of the granite. Seamus was brought down to his knees, with the cheers of the peelers lost in the groans of the Islanders.

Mickileen raised his hand to command attention, saying,

* *bawneen:* a short coat made of homespun white flannel

"If the wrestlers have no objection, we'll have a break to wet our throats." The crowd clapped this suggestion. Seamus stood up as straight as a candle, well-knit and brawny was he. He rubbed the knee that was bare through a rip in his pants, his eye catching a glance of the bright love of his heart watching nearby.

"Toss this thimbleful back, boy, and get out of your daydreaming," said Mickileen, nudging him.

While Seamus had the mug to his lips, a verse of a Gaelic song came to his ears:

The time will surely come when the Gael will have his own,
And the English will be driven from our native shore.

That verse stirred him as nothing else could. The blood sang through his veins and he said, "I'll never let down my native village."

In the next round, the rivals were more in earnest, each man watching a chance for an opening.

"God be with you, lad. Think of all the good and true men who came before you," shouted the villagers. "Now or never."

Excitement was at a high pitch. Seamus had the sergeant locked in a clinch, threw him back, had him down on the rod of his back and calling out, "Have you enough yet?" The servant of the Crown gave up. The bawneen-clad men cheered lustily, and they were aglow with joy.

"Throw this back, flower of men," smiled Mickileen, handing the victor the mug. Everyone was pushing and talking, trying to be close enough to shake the hero's hand. His admirers were for carrying him on their shoulders through the village, but he said with a smile, "No need for that yet, much more has to be done." His simple talk put the villagers in a calmer mood, and they cheered him again and again.

In a short time the peelers marched up the old road and back to the barracks. The villagers started to fill kegs, cruiskeens and bottles out of the puncheon.

We had planned to find a boat at nightfall, get the barrel aboard, sail into Duck Island and bury it. The evening was ideal, but where was the help? Paudeen, Mickileen and the Changeling were curled up between two boulders. Old Coilin, Luke and O'Cooney were snoring loud and hidden away in a bush of rushes. Men were stretched on all sides, and women trying to rouse them up and bring them home.

In the dark of the night, lads and colleens were dancing and enjoying themselves on the flat rocks. Then the peelers returned with strong reenforcements and seized the puncheon without any trouble. It was like throwing stones at the moon to resist them.

"Sure, the shore might be full of rum in the morning, and we'll have enough and plenty to spare," said the Rover, as the peelers rolled what was left in the puncheon away.

*

I used to work on the sea, fishing and gathering sea-weed. Many is the lesson I learned from the Atlantic that could not be found in the mighty seats of learning. The marine creatures that lived in the deep held great interest for me, and often when I should be working in the field, I took a stroll down to the shore to find out what was going on there.

One afternoon when the tide was out, I heard a clatter-ing under the chin of a rock. I stooped and peered into a cleft but could see nothing at all. I shoved in my hand. Surprise turned my hair into a stiff brush. The pain went to my heart when something grabbed my finger. The more I tugged, the harder it dug into the bone. I howled, and with one frantic effort I pulled free with the claw of a big red crab still holding my finger. My forefinger was cut to the bone, but I was glad that I had not lost it en-tirely. Unlike the crab who could grow a new one, I would have to do without mine. And that was how I learned to respect the crab.

Another bright day and I rambling around down at low-water mark when a strange creature appeared. It looked like a lobster. But in my eagerness to catch him, I plunged into the water, and with the hurry my foot slipped into a cleft. I was up to my armpits and the tide rising. I tried every way to free myself but to no avail. My cries for help caught the ear of Darach Mor, and he on his way home with a boatload of laminaria.

"What in the devil ails you at all that you didn't untie

your fong and pull your foot out of the bloody boot?"
he shouted, anchoring his boat and diving down with an
open knife in his hand to cut the fong. On coming to the
surface, he spouted a mouthful of water into my face.
"You are the dumbest creature that God ever put breath
in!"

"Find my boot for me now," I cried when my foot was
free.

But he only grabbed me fiercely, pitched me into his
boat on the top of my head and slapped me on the backside with his big palm, shouting, "Maybe you can write
stories, but you are as dumb as an ox."

At last, when I had freed my head out of the wet slimy
seaweed in the hold, I tried to speak to him. He was at the
helm and roared again: "Take the gallon and bail out the
water from the aft platform. Get a move on." I was so
afraid that I obeyed at once and kept my mouth shut until we landed at the little pier. I jumped out quickly and
ran home with one boot on and the other in a fissure at
the bottom of the sea.

One fine morning, my father stood at the cottage door
and said: "As the day is fine, Jimeen, carry up the five or six
small cocks of laminaria in the shore garden to the big
stack up on the hillock. Tar the pucan also. Let the tar to
the boil first and mix some wax through it to give the coat
a glossy sheen. You can also paint the woodwork inside.
The brushes and paint are on the table."

"Won't tomorrow be time enough to carry the weed
up?" I grumbled, gazing out through the window at the
smiling sea.

"Don't be talking like that, son, for the day is long,"
said he, hurrying away to work with the weed in the
strand.

While I carried the keg of tar and the turf to the shore, the birds sang and the bees hummed with joy in the warm sunshine, free from the meshes of authority. How I wished then to be either a bird or a bee. On reaching the shore, I kindled a turf fire beside a rock, filled the pot with tar and mixed some wax through. Our pucan was resting on the smooth oval stones nearby with a few blocks spaced apart under the keel and a smooth stone under her belly. First, I must wipe her skin clean with a burlap bag. When the tar-pot came to the boil, I added a little more wax and took it over to the boat's side and dipped the mop in it. After tarring a while, I took a few steps backward to look. "It is only like the cove below compared to the bay," I moaned, drying the sweat off my face with my sleeve.

The tar grew thicker and I needs must put the pot on the fire again. Glad for a moment of rest, I gazed out on the rippling water. A breeze had sprung up and two pucans were tacking down the bay. With full sails they were a fine sight to watch.

"Your soul from the devil, the pot is ablaze," a voice shouted, startling me out of my dream. "Hurry, hurry, and throw the old burlap bag on it." The bag smothered the flames.

"Thank you, Paddy. Faith, but you have a good head," I said to my friend who had happened along just in time.

"I learned that from my father the day he was tarring the boat and saw his reflection in the tar-pot. He was so taken with his own image, tipping his head this way and that way, that the dudeen fell from his mouth into the boiling tar. Flames leaped up, but he had the presence of mind to strip off his bawneen and smother the blaze with it."

"But what is the matter with you today?" he asked with a puzzled look.

"I can't go anywhere until the boat is tarred," replied I.

"By the deer, but that will take some time."

"Give me a hand, a chara,* and I'll do as much for you some other day."

"May God give you a spark of sense," he laughed, pushing back his mop of tow-colored hair from his eyes.

"If you take the swab for a few minutes I'll give you my little jackknife."

"Don't waste your breath," he grinned, hurrying away.

Indeed, the day was lovely. The small gardens along the shore were a-wearing of the green, speckled with yellow primroses and white-fringed daisies. The surface of the cove flashed like a gleam from glass, and the hot air quivered by the beach like the glowing of a hot lime kiln. I walked on down and sat on the edge of the pier thinking queer thoughts. While peering down at the bottom, I noticed a party of green crabs crowding around an old boot. The wonder of the world came over me as I saw them lift it up and scamper away with it. May God not weaken ye, brave little workers, said I to myself. A hunk of fish that had lodged inside the old boot caused this spell of work. They dragged their treasure into a hole in the pier. To be sure they are not lazy like me, thought I, strolling back to the boat.

In a short time Seaneen-Pat came up the strand at a hop and a skip. I kept rubbing the swab back and forth and humming a Gaelic lullaby. "Toor-aloor-aloo, the Fairies are coming . . ."

"Tarring today?" he mocked, putting a cheek on himself. I gave him a deaf ear.

"What could the matter be with you?" he shouted.

"Oh, it is yourself that's in it," exclaimed I, turning

* a chara: friend

--20--

around to face him with wonder in my eyes. I started to tar again.

"Are you going to play football, or will you go for a good swim?" I knew very well that they could not play any football, for the ball was in my possession. "Never mind now," laughed I, dipping the mop and holding it over the mouth of the pot to drip.

"Give me the ball, then," he begged, taking a step toward me.

"When she is out on the anchor-bed," said I, nodding at the boat, "many is the man that'll notice her."

Seaneen kept his mouth shut and looked at me puzzled.

"The Big Captain himself will be here soon to sail out in her," smiled I, laying down the swab, walking over to a flat stone and stirring a can of green paint with a cipeen.*

"Where are you going to put the green?" he asked, grabbing one of the brushes.

"Not at all," I snapped, snatching the brush out of his hand.

"Will you let me tar a little?" he asked, and I could feel his hot breath on the back of my neck, and I stooping over the tar-pot.

"I will not."

Just then, Paddy Colm reappeared along with a few more of the boys. I was painting the upper woodwork with Seaneen watching me.

"Let me paint a little," pleaded Seaneen as he climbed aboard with his dirty feet.

"Don't bother me," I shouted, rubbing the brush back and forth without raising my head. "I have this boat to tar and paint, and it must be done right. Can't you understand that?"

* *cipeen:* a small stick

~ 21 ~

"Give us the football, then," they chorused.

I took the curve out of my back and said softly, "I have the ball and it will stay with me until I'm finished. Now boys, if ye'll give me a hand with those tiny cocks of weed," pointing with the mop, "ye can have the ball and paint too."

They agreed at once.

I climbed upon the big stack to pitch down the cover of black weed that was there to protect the valuable laminaria from the rain. The top of the stack would be dry enough in the evening, and my father would build on it the laminaria we were drawing. One would think now that the loads were crawling up the green sward on their own, for the lads were hidden under the tangled masses of the dark ribbons of laminaria.

Many hands, they say, make light the work, and that is how it was with us. Even those who came late stayed. But to make a long story short, the boat was tarred and painted and the weed was heaped at the foot of the big stack by midday. Then we ran to the strand for a swim and a game of rounders, also a football match in the evening.

*

We lads used to give our ears to hair-raising tales out on the briny deep. Galore wild stories we would hear until we too longed to be out on the big sea with nets, spillers and hardlines. The chance to prove our knowledge came one day when we had the use of our house all to ourselves. It was Pat son-of-Bartly who suggested: "Let's try this game of fishing. We can make out that the table is a boat. The lines are on the loft, and all we need is some bait."

"A bright thought," nodded Paddy, and all hands agreeing there and then.

A couple of the boys found cans and hurried to the shore for limpets, winkles and crabs. Others were cutting a griddle cake and pouring milk into bottles for the crew's meal on the stormy sea. The little children who were to be the fish were given a lesson on how to behave in the deep.

"Beware now, you small fish, and don't be too greedy at first. Swim back and forth, and don't forget the right approach to the bait. If ye can nibble away and leave the hook clean, so much the better. Give a wee tug now and again," the teacher said, tugging at the line, showing them how it was done.

The sporty little fish goo-gooed with delight for having this grand part in the play. They swam around the table in circles, and we moored our boat right in the middle of the creek. We had a coil of red rope on deck and the end tied to a stone. Seaneen Mickil, Pat Bartly, Paddy Colm and myself made up the crew. Indeed, the deck was scarce enough for us when the lines, bait and food were stowed in their respective places.

"There is no sign of fish here," Paddy moaned, pitching out the mooring stone that hit the floor. "Not one black or white bird, not even a sea pig, God help us. I'll let another fathom of scope with the rope. That speckled bottom astern looks promising," said he, shielding his eyes with his open palm and peering down.

"You should be more careful when letting the mooring stone out. You have scared the fish," Pat warned, glaring at Seaneen. "You threw that stone as if you desired to kill. My back is wet to the skin with the splash you raised."

"There are a few birds back from our stern now and some sea pigs, too." (Two hens had jumped on the half-door to get away from the pigs who were grunting).

"Good signs," I nodded, putting a bait on my hook and casting out my line.

"I feel," whispered Seaneen. "Don't make so much noise breaking those winkles or you'll scare the fish away."

"One must put up a back bait," snapped Pat, the winkle-breaker, "and spare the crabs. Breams might come under us with the slack tide."

"A fat wrasse might be roaming around at the foot of the Little Wave," Paddy said, as he coiled his line and swished it deftly through the air until it landed at the Little Wave, really the hob.*

"A strong tug," gasped Seaneen, glancing around with wonder in his big blue eyes.

"Fish might bite better with the turn of the tide," remarked Pat.

"Listen to the music of the Little Breaker. The tide has already turned when she sings."

* *hob:* fireplace

The cricket had started to chirp in the hob. Myself was leaning over the gunwale watching the fish down on the bottom.

"Are you going to be seasick, Jimeen?" asked Patty, handing me a hunk of griddle cake.

All at once the line was pulled out of Pat's hand.

"Your soul from the devil, pull, pull!" shouted Pat. "Are you falling asleep? Put the steel in him, you rascal."

A sharp screech. Then another and another. By this time I had one struck too, and a lively one. He jumped and capered around with a pitiful "meeauve."

The Rover, who happened to be passing near the house, heard the cries and yowls, hurried in and looked around perplexed. "Ye pack of red devils," he shouted, taking out his knife and cutting the line at the back of the hook, coaxing the iron out of the child's lip. "What in the world made ye do such a thing? See now how it is with the poor child!" The Rover stepped upon a chair and reached to a rafter for some cobwebs, which he laid on the cut to stop the flow of blood. "Don't cry, a stór, and I'll bring you some sweets from the shop. There's a good boy, don't cry and you'll be well soon again when your Mama comes home."

More trouble was found with the cat and the hook in his jaw, but after a deal of coaxing we had the steel out. To be sure, the fishing was all over. We wound up the lines on the frames, tidied the place and took the boat back to the pier.

Little Peter's lip was swollen under a heap of cobwebs, but he was already playing with his pals who looked upon him as a hero. Poor pussy was left alone as he would not let a spider's web touch him, but trusted in Nature.

But for the Rover, little Peter would have suffered much—we would never have thought of pulling the hook out by the shank. Indeed, the Rover was noble. We never again heard about the incident, which placed him high in our esteem.

It is no lie to say that boys will be boys from Adam's day down to this. Even he himself who had grown a beard and had his choice and fill of everything good under the sun stole an apple. Is it any wonder then that we, young, foolish and as wild as colts, were up to all kinds of mischief?

We were chiefs of the ocean and lords of the shore. The smiling sea to the southwest, with small lonely islands, was an unknown region waiting to be explored by us: Duck Island and Muskerry, the Isle of Barra and Eagle Rocks where duilisg,* laver and periwinkles galore could be found. Often we searched for bits of wrack and kindled a fire. Nor did hunger ever bother us. A search among the weed-coated rocks at low water often rewarded us with lobsters and crabs. We could also snare rabbits at the sand dunes and catch birds with a crib. In the fine white sand on the beach where the seabirds had their nests, we found fresh eggs laid that morning. Bees galore flitted around on the clover blossoms, and honey could be found in nests of yellow moss in the glen. We often had a course of the sweet honey served in empty scallop shells to finish off the meal. Then we would swim and play games to our heart's content.

A strong desire came upon us one day to visit Carriage-mackan, a small island six miles to the south of our own. It was a great adventure, for we never had been there be-

* *duilisg:* edible seaweed

fore. We took the curach* and rowed out to this wild rock. Not a blade of grass was on it—just large round boulders and a kind of wild cabbage and beet that grew through the slits in the rocks where the seabirds made their nests. On reaching the far-off shore, we wandered around till we came to a headstone marking a grave.

"What a lonely spot he has," said Pat Bartly, going on his knees to say a prayer. Paddy and myself did the same.

"The poor sailor is here all alone for hundreds of years, perhaps, far away from his home and friends on this rock midway between Aranmore and Conamara," said I, examining the marker to see if there was any writing. Not a word.

"I wonder how was he found?" Paddy asked.

"Boats used to land here after the storms of the winter looking for wrack, and that is how it was when the body was found," explained Pat. "The storytellers claim that the corpse was kept covered with seaweed by the wild birds."

Nor did anyone ever discover what had happened to the vessel the sailor was on. Another mystery of the big sea. Faith, but he has a desolate spot in a big slit in the rock, especially in the winter when no boat can land and the breakers roar and crash wooly-white against the dark cliffs, the seals bellow with hunger, and the gulls, terns, penguins and cormorants are busy with their own private affairs.

As we rowed home in the evening, Aranmore lay curled on the horizon in a bluish haze—that enchanted island that rose from the depths of the Atlantic thousands of years ago to keep a lonely vigil at the mouth of Galway Bay.

* *curach:* canoe

28

Another misty morning as we were rowing out to Muskerry Island, a thick fog closed in on us and we could not see a boat's length ahead. Fear gripped us that we might miss the isle and find ourselves lost far out at sea. The mist was growing thicker and thicker. We decided to anchor. All at once, a dolphin jumped into the curach. Soon other dolphins began to bump our bottom, and one put his head on the gunwale, making strange noises. The one on board began answering with queer moans, shivering as if in pain. Before we knew from heaven above what to do, there was a new born beside her gasping for breath. The mother calmed down at once, looking on to see that all was well. We tried to pitch the mother out, and one of us lifted up the baby as if to pitch him out, too. Mama dolphin lifted her head to reach him and out they went. A school of dolphins jumping nearby tossed the baby high in the air with their snouts, seming to enjoy themselves as if celebrating the occasion. At last the fog cleared. We pulled in the grapnel and rowed our curach to the island.

That Sunday the friendly dolphins met us as usual at the Point, jumping and frolicking around the boat until we landed on Muskerry Isle. Indeed, we did not have a care in the world aboard Sean Pheggy's old boat, which we had borrowed unbeknownst to him. At last the old tub ran up on the strand, making a tinny noise over shells and pebbles. It was sultry now and we went swimming in our bare skins to cool off. The dolphins came around, diving under us and lifting us out of the water in a playful mood. Later on, as we rambled around looking for a nice place to build a hut, we saw a boat coming toward us from the north.

"O'Cooney," said Paddy. He thinks that the poteen-makers are here.

"Not at all," added Pat. "Catch him straining himself on an oar. Can't you see the graceful strokes of the Rover?"

"A hundred thousand welcomes, a chara," we shouted, racing down to the shore, pulling up the curach so that the Rover could step out on the dry strand.

"How did you know that we were here?" we asked.

"As the day was fine I thought of going looking for some rabbits," the Rover answered, taking a burlap bag out from the aft platform. "But let's first find the crabs."

We turned some stones and found several large green crabs, and then hurried to the sand dunes. On arriving there, the Rover stooped to smell the tiny tracks in the sand. He took out of his pocket a stump of candle, a ball of string and a tiny bell; tied the end of the string to the bell and candle and lit the latter; took a big crab out of the bag, spilled a few drops of candle grease on his back and set the candle there. Then fastening a bit of smelly fish over the crab's mouth he gave him a push, saying, "Follow your nose, a chara."

"The rabbits will wonder on seeing the lighthouse coming toward them in the dark," chuckled Paddy Colm, guarding the net covering the mouth of the burrow.

"A hungry crab is a clever lad too," I put in. "Should he find a cockleshell a bit opened on the strand, he'll take a pebble in his claws and push it into the slit. The shell will never close again, so the wily crab will have his meal."

"He is wise," agreed the Rover. "I remember one afternoon when I was making a shortcut through the shore. Suddenly I stopped with wonder. Right there as plain as day the head of a clay pipe was moving along the bottom of a rock pool. It hid from sight under a branch of seaweed. Why would the head of a pipe do that? I caught it easy enough and was surprised to find a live hermit crab inside! A flat lid of shell covered the mouth of the pipe, with the claws of the tenant sticking through. *Made in Eire* was marked in the chalk. For the sake of the crab I put it back again where I had found it."

"The crafty crab can fool you," said Mickileen. "I remember once seeing a number of lights moving around on the ground, and my hair began to push the old cap off my head. I turned on my heel to run and happened to meet Martin son-of-Nora, who was looking for wrack. The two of us plucked up enough courage to go back. What we found was a party of shore crabs dining on a rotten ray. The glowing lights were the phosphorescence from the crabs."

Just then two rabbits rushed headlong into the net, interrupting the Rover.

"They are full of fat," said he, putting them into the bag. "We'll have a fine meal later on." And so we did.

The day came when we boys had our little house built, thatched with rushes from the glen and everything in its place. Were we the happy and carefree lads with lashings of good food to eat! How we loved that lonely island.

One day in the autumn great wonder came over us when we landed. Was our hut on fire? As we hurried toward it we noticed half a score of wild-looking men clad in homespuns and gathered around a fire with a big pot simmering on it. Our hut nearby was filled with the utensils for distilling poteen.

"What right have ye men to take our hut?" we shouted as one.

"God bless ye, friends of my heart, we'll all have a merry time yet but have a little patience," smiled a middle-aged man with a black beard. "The courage is right there," he said, nodding at the pot on the fire and cracking his knuckle joints one after the other.

One man was feeding little clods of turf to the fire, keeping the caldron at the right boil. The worm passed like a corkscrew through a barrel of cold water, which cooled the vapor into liquid that trickled from the lip of the worm into an oaken tub. Blackbeard found a pitcher and treated us in a generous manner.

"Here is good health to ye, lads. Toss it back before it cools."

The poteen had a burnt peaty flavor and tingled through our veins. In a short time we were tipsy galore.

"Where is O'Cooney now, that schemer who gave ye the hut? Or was he bold enough to do such a thing?" shouted Paddy Colm. He started to talk without any sense, eyes sunk back in his head, the sweat on his face glistening in the firelight. Fresh maggots caused by the mountain dew began to crawl in his brain so that his talk made no sense. In short, he was going to fight the poteen-makers.

"Quarreling is no good, a chara," advised a stocky distiller who had such a long dark mustache that he could easily tie the ends of it at the back of his head. "Silence now and we'll have a verse of a song," announced he.

"Raise it up, a stór," urged Long Mustache.

There was clapping of hands from us all as Blackbeard cleared his throat and began to sing in the Gaelic:

Oh Paddy dear an did you hear the news that's going round,
The shamrock is forbid by law to grow on Irish ground.
No more Saint Patrick's day we'll keep, His color can't be seen,

*They're hanging men and women for the wearing of the
    green.
And since the color we must wear is England's cruel red—
Sure Ireland's sons will ne'er forget the blood that they
    have shed.*

That is all we heard, for we were dead to the world in
a drunken sleep.

When we had not returned by the light of day, our people at home began to worry about us. The Rover hinted
that on such a fine day we might have gone in on the island. At last, with encouragement from him, they sailed
in. It was a moonlit night and they, finding us stretched
on the sandy beach in a deep sleep from the barley juice,
carried us down to the boat like so many sacks of oats. Did
we get a tongue-lashing from our parents after our senses
returned! We were warned about the evils of drink, and
we had to promise that we would never again make beasts
of ourselves with the poteen.

The bonfire night is an old custom among the Gaels, and we boys eagerly awaited its arrival on the twenty-third of June. Although we have no record of its origin, yet we have ample proof that this holiday—St. John's Eve as it is called—is older than Christianity. The Druids had lighted fires long before the coming of St. Patrick. When this Holy Man landed on the coast of County Wicklow, he kindled a fire in honor of Easter. He did not know that he was breaking the pagan law, which forbade the lighting of any fire until the signal was given by the fire of the Druids first lighted on a green hill. The chief of the Barony saw the Saint's fire in the distance. He sent for the seer at once to find out what was to be done. "Our law has been broken for the first time," the wise man said gravely. "If that flame on the old hill of Slane is not put out tonight, it will never again be extinguished in Eire."

It is the custom now, as it was then, to celebrate St. John's Eve. For weeks before that day we boys collected pieces of wrack, bones and old baskets for the big fire. On the Holy Eve crowds of young and old were making their way, stooped down from the baskets of turf they were carrying, to Cranmor, the highest hillock in the village.

The smoke from the village houses was going straight up to the blue sky. The harsh cry of "draoch, draoch" from the corncrake in the meadow mingled with the few last notes from a blackbird who hopped from a rock into a blackthorn bush where she had hidden her nest. The pale moon, moving up in a star-flecked sky, caused a patch of placid water of the bay to flicker silvery like the scratched scales of breams. Dogs barked louder than usual seeing the stir among the villagers carrying loads. Old Paudeen's dog had attacked Mickileen Liam when he caught him filling a basket of turf in his master's rick. Oscar was unaware that his master knew about it, and Mickileen had to run for his life.

"Let us spare the paraffin and have a blaze to lick the sky when the other fires are low," said Pat Bartly when the mountain of turf, bones and wrack were kindled.

All agreed.

Fires were kindled now on every hillock as far as the eye could see. Old Coilin took out his Rosary beads, a signal for us all to go on our knees.

"We put ourselves under your protection, Oh Holy Mother of God and blessed Saint John," he began.

It was soothing and pleasant to listen to the Gaelic prayers in the stillness of the night, while the wavering flames lit the solemn faces around and they responding. When the Rosary was finished, the old people left for home.

Fires galore were blazing now, casting their glow on the peaceful Atlantic as it washed the feet of the headlands. Up to now we had been sparing of the oil: Who knows what reserves the other bonfires might have?

While I was gazing out to sea the old lobster pots in the Changeling's barn came to my mind.

"Pat," I whispered, "has the Changeling any use for those pots in his barn?"

"Arrah, they are only coming in his way."

In no time at all we were racing to the barn. We paused at the door, for it was dark inside.

"What is that?" whispered Seaneen Mickil, putting an ear on himself to hear better.

"Rats!" replied Pat. "Near the shore here is full of them, and they can swim and dive, too."

"Too much noise for rats," said I.

"It might be wild cats," mumbled Seaneen.

Paddy Colm's hand touched mine in the darkness and he screamed.

"Is it trying to waken the whole village ye are?" asked Pat, in an angry whisper.

We left the barn, each of us carrying two pots. Suddenly the sharp cry of some small animal startled us.

"A weasel is killing a helpless rat," said Paddy.

While crossing the Changeling's meadow we heard the crash of stones.

"Look over there!" Pat whispered, pointing his arm.

But we saw nothing in the darkness.

It was deep in the night now and only a few fires were still blazing.

"See that one across the bay? The flames are licking the stars above," exclaimed Pat.

"They think we are near dead," Seaneen added, taking a pot and throwing a dash of paraffin on it.

Wavering tongues of flames from the pots and paraffin were escaping to heaven itself, giving such a light down the slope from us that one could take a tiny thorn from his finger if it was there.

"Nothing like this was ever seen in Conamara since the Saint himself lit the first fire on the hill of Slane," Pat boasted, nodding at the blaze with his eyes shut.

"True," I agreed, pitching an armful of oil-soaked turf into the flames. "Any ship that is near the coast might mistake ours for a lighthouse."

One by one the other fires were dying down. Some of the colleens from the village joined us, and with hands

~~36~~

clasped and heads bowed, we shuffled slowly around the fire reciting the Rosary.

When we had finished the prayers we sprinkled the holy water. Then we filled our buckets with red embers and hurried to the fields. As I walked sunwise around our cabbage patch, I pitched in a few embers saying in a solemn tone, "Blessed Saint John, make this garden fruitful, in the name of the Father, and of the Son and of the Holy Ghost. Amen."

The Changeling talking down in the kitchen and the dog barking woke me up the next morning. The dog always went for him because when the Changeling spoke a rumble would come from his throat, and Watch would think that he was going to fight.

"I am ruined after the night," he growled. "Fine seasoned pots and many is the hard day I put into weaving them. Not one of them would I give today for a silver crown. Who would ever think that the boys would do such an evil thing?"

"Some of the lads in this world know not which sky is nearer to them," Daida replied, then called me.

I put on my gray petticoat* in a hurry, trying to think what explanation I would give.

"What came over you to steal this man's lobster pots and burn them?" shouted Daida. Turning to the Changeling, he said in a serious tone, "Get them all in the Black Hole. The English prison might teach 'em a lesson."

"Don't scare the boy," advised the Changeling, growing restless on the chair.

Watch, who was lying under the table, raised his head and growled. The Changeling turned around quickly and

* *gray petticoat:* the customary garment worn by boys through the age of twelve

~ 37 ~

whispered, "It was Tameen son-of-Antoine who told me, and I settled with the old man for two florins."

"The fairy devil is a schemer," exclaimed Pat when I met him down on the strand that evening. "He made a pound easy enough, and if he bought ducks with the money, they would drown no doubt. He had offered the same old trash to Red James for a shilling each, and Red told him that he would not like to lose his ropes and corks, for the ballast would spill out through their rotten bottoms."

"The Changeling must have seen us take them," I put in. " 'Twas he who had knocked down the wall when we heard the crash that you saw in the dark."

"To be sure it was," agreed Pat. "The lanky devil was well-pleased and there was no fear at all that he would stop us. Did he not earn a pound much easier than making kelp or fishing. No use talking now, but there will come another day."

"What do you think about Tameen?"

"What would you expect from the son of Tony of the small scabby potatoes," Pat Bartly growled, spitting on the palms of his hands and rubbing them together as he turned on his heels to go home.

*

I remember when as a wee lad the wonder of the world
was put on me the first Sunday I walked the three miles
to church along with Mama. Groups of women in red
petticoats and multicolored shawls and men in homespuns
were hurrying along the road as we drew near to the
chapel.

The church was nearly full when we walked in. A tall
gray-haired priest dressed in white vestments and a dark-
haired slim boy carrying a bucket of holy water shuffled
down the middle of the floor. With a long-handled brush,
the Holy Father sprinkled the women who stood on the
left-hand side first. Back in the rear was a gallery where the
nobility of the parish would sit in comfortable seats, while
we down below stood on the floor and no seats at all. His
Reverence seemed to be in no hurry here—he stood on
tiptoes throwing brush after brush to the gentry upstairs.
Did they need the holy water more than we, I wondered?
At last he walked hurriedly toward the altar, shaking the
empty brush so the men had to bless themselves with dry
fingers. The peelers up in the front of the gallery caught
my eye. I remembered how my father had fought with
them some time before when they tried to arrest him for
being in the Irish Land League. I wondered if the saucer
caps would be up front in Heaven, too.

"Mama," I whispered, nudging her with my elbow.
"Do you see where the peelers are?"

"Shush," she said, "or the priest will raise a temper and

throw us out. In the first place, you are supposed to be over on the men's side of the aisle. Did you know that?"

Just then the people rose from their knees ready to hear the sermon, and the Holy Father turned around toward the people. His face was kind of serious as he waited for the shuffling to quiet down.

"Give unto Caesar what is Caesar's and unto God what is God's," he began. "This text is taken from the Scripture, and it is my solemn duty to explain it to ye, my dearly beloved. It is also my duty to warn ye to keep out of secret societies which are at present and will be in the future a curse on our green land. No doubt, but ye have heard that a few families were evicted in the other end of this parish last week. To be sure, that was the will of the Almighty, and He will reward them in the Heaven of Graces for all their hardships and sufferings in this vale of tears. Dearly beloved, we must bow to the will of God."

A few polite coughs came from the body of the church.

"Every Christian should pay his debt. In the name of God, let ye all try to pay the rents and the landlord might be more lenient. In some parts of our dear country misguided young men take the law into their own hands. They do indeed, my dearly beloved. Sneaking around in the dark of the night, when they should be asleep in their beds and watched over by the good Lord. I warn ye now that it is a mortal sin to be out in the dead of night knocking down the walls of the big estates, firing into gate houses with intent to murder landlords, agents, bailiffs, herds and the peelers. It is also a grave mortal sin to drive thousands of bullocks off the big farms out on the roads or down the steep cliffs to be killed. Ah, my dearly beloved that will get ye nowhere but down to hell."

Some groans and the scratchings of hobnailed boots on

the hard floor could be heard from the body of the church.

"My dearly beloved brethren, if the tenants are evicted, it must be the will of our dear Lord."

"It is not the will of God," was shouted from the floor of the church. "God has nothing at all to do with it. Musha, what could the matter be with you, Father? Just examine your own conscience!"

His Reverence raised his head quickly, flushed, then paled.

"Who was it? Who was it? Who profaned God's house?"

"Leave God out of it," the same voice shouted again as he jumped nimbly on the Baptismal Font.

"God help us all," prayed the old priest. "Ah, it is yourself, Luke. My poor man, your mind has snapped. May the Lord look down with mercy on us and the Blessed Virgin keep us all in the State of Grace and sanity," said his Reverence in a sad tone, rubbing the gray stubble on his chin, and a look of worry came into his eyes.

"Men and women," shouted Luke, as the eager crowd milled around, "if ye have any drop at all of red blood in your veins, the only way we can save our families is to throw the millstone from around our necks and fight like men."

"May God not weaken you, Luke, for that is the talk with the skin on," was shouted from the body of the church.

"A hundred men could go through thousands of landlords, bailiffs and English soldiers and peelers just like a hawk through a flock of sparrows," shouted Luke, his blue eyes glistening like new steel.

"Hear—hear—forever Luke!" cheered the crowd.

"Hurrah—hurrah—hurrah. The land for the people and the road for the bullocks," sang the congregation, marching out of the chapel and following their leader in military formation.

The old priest was left alone by himself standing at the foot of the altar thinking sadly on how he had lost control of his flock. Mama and myself went on home along with the crowd. Indeed, I was tired enough of the long white road that Sunday, but I had many fine stories to tell my comrades about my first trip to the mainland.

✳

The two days that excited us lads the most came in March and November when we honored God's visit to our Island. It was a grand occasion the time the Stations* were called to be in our house. The walls had to be white-washed inside and out; tables and stools scrubbed and cleaned, fine white sand carried in baskets from the strand and spread in the path around the house.

On the day of the Stations, the neighbors began to arrive early, the older ones eager to find a place near the fire. Red James son-of-John, with a clipped red beard and closely cropped head for the occasion, stood at the gable end with a crowd around him. The Boatman and Darach Mor made a shortcut through the cabbage patch to join them.

"God bless ye," saluted Darach, climbing over the wall. "Is it not a green kind of morning?"

"Natural for this time of year," replied Martin O'Cooney, finding some trouble digging a clay pipe from the pocket of his brand-new vest. At last he held the dudeen between his teeth, lit a match with the nail of his thumb and sheltered it in the crook of his hand.

"Beware now!" whispered Darach, clasping the pipe. "Are you not going to receive?"

"See you that now," said Martin, letting the pipe drop and about to put the match in his pocket when his cronies chuckled.

* *Stations:* celebration of the Mass in a private home

"My dear man," smiled the Rover, "we all are a little forgetful, more so when we need a pull."

"Not a man on earth today has the tide going with him like the pale-faced Changeling," said Sean son-of-Pheggy. "He is inside the house with a cloud of smoke over him. He got leave from the old bishop to have a smoke before receiving, because of a disease."

"Disease my eye!" shouted O'Cooney, taking a stretch out of his neck. "The lanky fairy dev——"

"Shush, shush," interrupted Darach, putting his hand over O'Cooney's mouth. "Don't curse until the service is over."

"The Holy Fathers should be here any minute now," remarked Sean Pheggy, tugging at the brown tuft of goat's whisker on his chin and glancing east toward the shore.

The shore looked dark and dreary. Laminaria weed bleached white by sunshine and showers, and the red and black weed, spread out for a fertilizer, gave the fields a speckled look. Thrushes were hopping about in the cabbage patch moaning with the hunger.

"Arrah, here they come now," warned the burly Boatman.

The parish priest, lean and tall, his shoulders a bit stooped from age, strode in state ahead. The curate, same in width as in height and the prick of a gooseberry thorn would take blood from his rosy face, was trying hard to keep up. When the Holy Fathers entered the house, the people rose to their standing and bowed.

"Many a céad míle fáilte, hundred thousand welcomes, Father," could be heard from the kitchen as the clergy took off their coats and replied, "May ye all live long in health, friends."

A hearty turf fire glowing on the hearth caused the

white sand spread on the floor to glitter. Since the chairs and stools had been removed, the kitchen was roomy. Only a dresser and chest were left near the wall. The curate went into the parlor to "hear," but the parish priest stayed near the kitchen fire. The village women came bare-footed in bright red petticoats and multicolored shawls. Soon the kitchen was full and overflowing into the yard. Those outside knelt on one knee with a cap underneath to cushion it from the ground. A couple of the old women were reciting their beads aloud and pressing in on his Reverence in the nook.

The curate was fixing the table that was to serve as an altar. A big can of water was placed on a box at the end of the board. The young priest clad in white garments put a purple stole around his neck and read the holy Latin words over the vessel, pitching in a cupful of salt. Darach Mor was holding the vessel as the curate dipped a brush in it and sprinkled the faithful with a broad sunwise sweep of his right arm.

Galore of the men had crowded around the parlor door, each sinner trying to outdo his neighbor to be heard first. In the other corner were the women who desired to be heard by the parish priest, who they figured had the greatest power to forgive. A bit of a scuffle began when two resolute women arose from their knees at the same time, the agile one leaping over a kneeling sinner to win her place in line. Molly Bawn, a handsome lass broad enough in the beam, had been thrust back twice, first when the scarecrow just heard had blocked her path and now by Ann.

"Mhuirre, Mhuirre, Virgin Mary, oh to be bested by frail little Ann," Molly moaned, glancing warily around. Then she spied a chest with a net heaped on it at the back of the old priest. As the house rose from their knees and moved toward the altar, Molly tiptoed over behind them. She climbed up on the chest to make a shortcut, but with the hurry she tripped and fell between the chest and the wall. Those who had heard the thud turned their heads. The parish priest did the same and said "Oh, oh," out loud. The congregation shuffled nearer and saw one foot sticking up, the big toe caught in the meshes of the net. The poor girl was standing helpless on her head.

"What is this?" whispered the Rover, his face redder than the petticoat that had dropped down over Molly's breasts. He took off his bawneen, pitched it deftly to cover her shame and freed the toe out of the meshes. The whole house was by now watching, more interested in Molly's act than in the Holy Mass.

"Face the altar, will ye? Or are ye a bunch of pagans!" the parish priest said sternly. Then helping Molly to her feet, he asked kindly, "Are you hurt, my good woman?"

She did not reply, but stared wild-eyed around, as if expecting someone to answer for her.

"What in the world came over you, Molly? Why did you stand on your head in the hole and put on an act?" asked the Rover, putting on his bawneen.

"I don't know," she whispered in a shaky voice. "I'm sorry. But I was determined to be heard."

"You were heard and seen, too," smiled the Rover.

Some had the corners of their bawneens stuck in their mouths to hold back the laughter.

"Let ye all go on your knees and be quiet," said the priest severely.

The crowd moved back and someone was pushed against the box that held the can. The holy water ran all over the floor. The old priest was now placing a long stool as a kind of buffer between himself and the sinners. In the hubbub, Barbara, daughter of ninety-year-old Liam, lost her balance and knocked down the stool. Old Nora screamed, "I'm killed dead," for the stool had fallen on her naked foot. While his Reverence was consoling her, the stole fell from his neck. "That's it behind your backside, Father," called out O'Cooney, pointing his finger.

"Don't speak talk like that to a priest," said Darach Mor in a low tone.

"Only a slip of the tongue. Faith but the dev——"

"Shush," whispered Darach, again trying to put his foot on O'Cooney's to warn him against cursing. Instead he pressed his hobnailed boot down on Una Phaudeen's bare foot. Una shrieked with pain, then took a pin from her hair and pushed it into O'Cooney's own backside. He jumped and stared around at Sean Pheggy who he thought had done it.

"Wait until the Mass is over and my soul from the devil."

"Let there be a little manners on ye," interrupted the Holy Father sharply. "It is a shame for ye to be acting like this and God visiting, or is the Big Boy kindling ye?"

A couple of the men had the floor dried up and were shaking dry sand under the feet of the flock. The curate, perspiring freely, was saying the Mass. Most of the faithful had been heard. The old priest was serving the Mass as well as hearing the confessions. On a chair at his side was the small brass bell to be rung at the Consecration.

Myself, at that time the little man of the house, wandered around through all of this, wondering galore at the strange goings on. The shiny yellow bell caught my eye. I lifted it to have a look underneath and the ring of it put the heart across in me. I put it down in a hurry and looked around. The people had their heads bowed, thumping their breasts. Fear gripped me as I looked into the priest's face.

"Don't do that anymore, little man," he whispered.

But the faint smile on his face gave me courage to move out of his way.

When the service was over, the faithful made a dash for the can of holy water that had been refilled after the accident. As the men and women shoved and jostled each other, one could hear the sounds made by the bottles, with the water gurgling in. Darach Mor placed a chair at the table and wiped the seat of imaginary dust with a white handkerchief. Then the parish priest sat down, took a small black book from an inside pocket and began to turn the pages. He stopped, smoothed out the page with the back of his hand, and hovered over it with the pencil. "Mickileen Liam," he called, glancing around.

"Coming, Father," spoke Mickileen, threading his way through the crowd, laying down a bright shilling on the table.

"Darach Mor."

"Present, Father." He made his way to the board and laid down two sixpenny bits.

"Martin O'Cooney," called the priest, wetting his thumb and turning over the leaf.

Martin looked wild-eyed around and up at the rafters as if sentenced to be hung. He said sadly, "I'm sorry, Father, but there is not a red penny at me just now. Yet with the help of God I'll pay you when I sell the pig."

"Hmm," replied his Reverence, wetting the point of the pencil. "I'll put a blank after your name as you never pay. But there is no want of money on you for poteen. You were tipsy galore coming home from the shebeen a few nights ago. What a sin and a shame for you, a grown-up man, to be acting so foolish."

"Father, who told you that, may I ask?" said Martin, scraping the floor with his boots and glaring at his neighbors, hoping to pick out the spy. "Some people are so good telling lies. Did they tell you, Father, that I had a fine slip of a pig, God bless her, and——"

"That'll do now," snapped his Reverence, raising his hand to command silence and glancing in the book. "Sean Pheggy."

"Here, Father," bowing and laying down a shilling.

When the collection was over, the Holy Father picked up the heap of silver and tied it up into a red handkerchief. He thanked the villagers for their generosity to God and prayed that they would be seven times better in health and substance that time again.

"Have you any news at all, Father, about any stroke of work?" asked the Boatman, rubbing his sideburns.

"Well, my friends," spoke the priest gently, "I am doing my utmost to find a loan from the Government to finish that old road yonder."

"We need a pier for our boats much more than we need a road," said the Boatman. "How can a road be made without stuff to blast the big rocks to the skies? Will the English allow us to have dynamite or powder?"

"Not at all," shouted the Rover. "They'd suspect that we'd use it on the militia or the peelers' barracks instead of the granite."

"Everyone knows that a pier can be built without blasting. Stones are plentiful on the shore and handy to be laid on top of each other," the Boatman went on persuasively.

"We do need a road badly, too," put in O'Cooney,

taking a stretch out of his neck to glance over those who stood in front.

"Do ye all hear himself?" sneered the Boatman. "No doubt but you do need a smooth level road coming home on dark nights full up to the Adam's apple and——"

"Close your big mouth, servant of the lies," O'Cooney roared, clenching his fists and raising them threateningly. "Only I'm after receiving and giving honor to——"

"Enough said, my friends," commanded his Reverence. "If we find a trifle of money, we could have a bit of pier and the road, too."

The curate came around now and called out the names of those who had not paid the "Oats Money" for his horse, though it was a bicycle he rode. Those who had not paid handed him a florin each. O'Cooney gave him his word of honor that he would be as good as the next when he sold the pig.

Daida invited some of the villagers to stay for the priest's dinner. One needs must be tactful in this delicate business so as to escape a social blunder. But to even things up, all the neighbors would be invited to the ceilidhe* that night.

Mama and a few young girls were busy now preparing the big meal. Truth to say there was choice food aplenty and the very best of liquor for the guests. Three ovens did not have a minute's rest the day before, baking bulogs† that were a golden hue from the eggs and speckled with raisins and currants; sweet eating pancakes galore, half-drowned in honey; pollack, cod, haddock, sole and halibut —fine and fresh-caught before dawn on a spiller; a goose huge and fat towered above everything else in the center

* *ceilidhe:* concert
† *bulog:* cake

—50—

of the table, and seven chickens along for company. China plates, cups and saucers that had not been out of the cupboard since the last Stations; silver knives, forks and spoons, which glittered in the light of two large speckled candles. Ah, the china teapot was a beauty, blue flowers handpainted on its brown sides. Indeed, it was not for beauty alone that it outshone all else, but for the noble tradition and romance attached to it. In the far distant past my mother had received it as a present from her Aunt Barbara, who happened to be in the United States at the time of the Civil War. When the Yanks invaded the south, Barbara's home was burned to the ground. Not one single article escaped the fire but the teapot. A Crucifix and some holy medals that had been stored in it saved it no doubt.

The guests sat around the table now, the parish priest at the head and the rest in regular order—not by rank or wealth as practiced in the big world outside, but by their knowledge of Gaelic lore and wit. Milk punch sweetened with sugar was prepared for the women. My father took another quart out of the cupboard, filled the glasses, and set them on the board.

"Good health to ye all," toasted the priest, rising to his standing. "And may ye be seven thousand times better in health and happiness this time again."

"Good health to yourself, Father, and may the good Lord spare you for a hundred more Stations," was chorused by the house, mingled with the tinkling of glasses. Owing to the long fast from the midnight before—a rule of the Catholic Church—great hunger was on them.

"Since it is yourself that reads the papers, Father," said Old Coilin, turning to the parish priest, "is there anything at all about this Home Rule now?"

"England is for the English first and always, and the heavy taxes she grabs from us keeps her idle rich in luxury," replied the Holy Father.

"Instead of giving freedom, Britain would have rivers of blood flowing and hills of dead piled up to add more land to her Empire," added Daida as he carved the goose and served her around. "Never will she part with an acre without a fight. Big ranches are fattening millions of bullocks and sheep. Those lands should by right be feeding Gaels instead of cattle."

"A small country like ours is no match for a mighty Empire," said the old priest hastily.

"Where did you leave the United States?" smiled Martin son-of-Anna, brushing back his thick dark hair with his palm.

"Have a spark of sense," spoke the Rover bitterly. "The rich Yanks and the English lords are just like this," putting up his two forefingers.

"I won't gainsay you in that," agreed the priest. "Even in the Boer War, just over, Uncle Sam took the side of John Bull."

"Pardon me, Father," interrupted Mickileen Liam, pulling a quarter from the chicken and laying it gently on the priest's plate. "I can see that you are not much of a hand to help yourself. To be sure we all know that the poor Boers were oppressed like ourselves, so that the rich lords could deck their ladies with diamonds and feathers like the rainbow." Mickileen continued rising to his standing and cutting a cake in slabs.

"I do think myself," spoke the curate, "that the halter next to the windpipe should be cut first. Take the big estates from the landlords and divide them among the poor peasants."

"Where would the peasants find the money to pay?" asked the old priest, rubbing the stubble on his chin.

"It's hard to get blood from a turnip," retorted Daida. "What did the landlords pay for the estates in the first place?"

"Not a penny," agreed the priest. "They evicted the poor and left them to die on the green hillsides."

"Can we not take our own land back from the robbers?" shouted Old Paudeen in an angry tone.

"All we need is to be united and true. Drive the bullocks off the big ranches in the dark of the night. Find a few muskets and make some noise outside the Big House. Only I'm in the state of grace now, I'd say much more," shouted Daida, hitting the corner of the table with his fist and setting the china and glasses dancing.

Mama, who was busy attending on the women, turned quickly around on hearing the noise. She grabbed the noble teapot that had survived the burning of Atlanta and examined it. "Ah," she whispered, "you are safe, thanks be to the Lord," fanning it with a white handkerchief as if it were a person who had fainted.

"If we are united, nothing can beat us," said Old Coilin. "I remember the cruel evictions of the year eighteen hundred and forty-nine when my poor father and his two brothers were thrown out of their homes to die."

My father filled the glasses and made a pitcher of hot punch for the women.

"Not a drip of it will touch my tongue, thank you," stammered Nan Bheag, looking the other way and reaching for the glass at the same time.

"Don't be so bashful," smiled Daida.

Nan swung the glass around so the sweetness would not delay on the bottom and tossed the drink back.

"Shyness on them colleens," chuckled the Rover. "One would think that the butter would not melt in their mouths, but if any of them were outside in the dark of the night with a——"

"Shush, hush," broke in the chuckling priest. "To be serious, I wonder myself why more couples are not stirring out this Spring."

"It has been said that the clergy are charging too much for tying the knot," mumbled Mickileen, looking up at the rafters.

The Holy Father laughed long and loud.

"I do think myself, your Reverence," added Nan, "if the couple are truly in love, the money for the splicing will be found in some way."

"I am with you in that, Nan," smiled the Rover.

The priest leaned over sideways, finding some trouble fishing a big silver watch out of his fob pocket.

"Oh-ho," he exclaimed. "Look at the time it is, and we never felt it passing. If we don't wish to make a day and a night of it, let us be going," he said, rising from the chair, yawning and stretching himself.

"Now, friends of my heart, we'll have deoch an dorais," * invited Daida, filling the tumblers.

"May we all be alive in good health this time twelve-month," toasted the parish priest.

"Amen," chorused the house, amid the tinkling of glasses as they touched.

"O'Cooney is down in the kitchen," whispered the Rover, who had just entered the parlor.

"Come right in, Martin," invited Daida.

O'Cooney walked shyly into the room with the old cap

* *deoch an dorais:* the drink at the door or the parting drink

~~54~~

squeezed in his hands against his breast. He bowed low
to the clergy.

"Throw this back," said Daida, handing him a glass of
poteen.

"Not a taste of that stuff will touch my tongue, thank
you," pushing the glass away with his hand and glancing
at the priest with a scared look. "I just ran up from the boat
to let ye know that she is a-swim," he said as he looked out
through the window.

"Thank you, Martin," smiled his Reverence. "Now be a
good sport and don't spoil the party. That thimbleful won't
shorten your life or keep you out of Heaven, either."

Martin's eyes lit up as he took the glass of poteen with a
quivering hand. He drank it and turned to run out when
Daida filled it again and whispered, "You stay right here
with the women, Martin. There is some of the goose left,
so help yourself."

The happy villagers talked and laughed as they escorted
the clergy down to the pier. On one side of the bohreen a
field sloped sharply down to the sea. A layer of fresh laminaria had been spread on it as a fertilizer.

"I'll take the shortcut," shouted Mickileen, jumping
over the wall.

"Two is company," laughed the plump curate, clam-
bering over the stone wall in spite of warnings.

Mickileen slipped down on his backside. The crowd
laughed heartily. The curate went to his aid but lost his
balance, rolled over and over, gathering momentum with
the slimy, slippery ribbons of laminaria twisting around
him, until he rolled over the cliff and into the sea. Mickileen jumped in after him to help. Neither of them was
hurt and they swam over to the nearby pier.

"Musha Father, you are half-drowned," said Old Coilin, glaring at Mickileen, who was walking back and forth with a sglug-sglag from his boots just as if they were talking to each other.

The curate was rocking all over with laughter trying to fix a suspender that had snapped. "That weed is very slippery, like——"

"Like the back of an eel, Father," added Coilin. "But none ever found a cold from the salt water."

It was a fine evening with a sharp sting in the air. Old Coilin, Mickileen Liam, Daida and the clergy stepped aboard. Sails were hoisted with a "Click-a-clack, click-a-clack" coming from the cheeves as Daida was hoisting the mainsail. The parish priest took the helm and turned the boat around sunwise. The main and jib bellied out with the light westerly and the boat heeled over as the main was sheeted home. The clergy and the boatmen kept waving their hats and caps to those on the pier, who in turn were waving handkerchiefs and caubeens* until the pucan was too far away heeled over by the press of sails and a ridge of snowy foam curling from her bows, until she disappeared heading for the mainland.

* *caubeen:* hat

These Holy Stations touched us boys and kindled our dramatic instinct, leaving us in living pain to imitate it. For all kinds of drama, we depended upon ourselves alone since no plays, circuses or cinemas ever appeared in our part of the world. Unlike the children of the big town whose creative instinct is blunted by too much entertainment, we were always looking for fresh outlets.

As we gathered one evening in the loft of a barn, Pat Bartly asked, "Where will the Stations be next?"

"Not in this village anyway," Paddy Colm replied. "And what a sin and a shame that we can't have them more often. Should I find death during the night, it is hundreds of years I'd have to spend in Purgatory."

"You'd be lucky to go there and not to the other place where you'd be chained in the red and flogged with brimstone flails," whispered Seaneen Mickil. "Your sins are nothing compared to mine. I smashed the Changeling's window with a rock and scared Old Coilin stiff by firing sods of turf at him in the dark of the night."

We looked at each other, then at Seaneen, who in turn looked above us at the barn rafters.

"To be sure we need a Station," said Pat. "But first we must rehearse."

Next Sunday we borrowed Old Paudeen's cottage when no one was there. Pat Bartly, or Father Pat as we called him now, was our pastor—elected by the free choice of his parishioners. This blessed morning, Father Pat wore an empty flour bag with a hole in the bottom for his head and one in each corner for the arms. The picture of a crowing rooster was on his Reverence's back, and under the bird was "112 pounds" printed in blue. In a half circle from the tip of the tail to the red comb of the cock was printed in red letters: THE TOP OF THE MORNING. Father Pat dusted and fixed the altar, setting a few holy pictures against the wall. Two tiny candles were stuck in two large turnips in the center of the board. Seaneen was at the gable end beating a tin can with a tholepin to warn laggards to hurry for the service. The Rover, who had come along as usual, stood in the back.

When the mass began you could have heard a pin falling. The priest lit the candles, genuflected before the altar, then turned to face the congregation with a solemn face. Myself, the altar boy, handed him a new brush made of straw. His Reverence dipped it into a bucket of seawater and made a broad sunwise sweep of his arm so that even those in the rear could catch a few drops. After giving the house his blessing, he bowed, swung around on his heels and opened O'Rafferty's book of Gaelic poetry where a green ribbon showed between the leaves. The kitchen was full of boys, plus the Rover, who was on his knees at the back door.

At the Gospel the faithful stood up and Father Pat delivered a stirring sermon on "Rome was not built in a day."

"My dearly beloved brethren," he began, making a few little coughs to clear his throat. "Every beginning is weak. But let us have patience and God's holy will will prevail. Was Rome built in a day?" Here he paused as if expecting an answer, but only a few coughs were heard so he continued: "Dearly beloved, it is necessary for us all to plan for the future, not only here but in faraway lands that are filled with wicked people who have wealth galore and enslave the poor."

The Rover interrupted the sermon now by hurrying over to tap the priest on the shoulder and put a whisper in his ear. The Holy Father raised his hand to command attention. Someone was outside listening at the back door. Father Pat blew out the candles, pulled the vestment over his head and handed it to the Rover. There was a sharp knock on the door.

"Get up and bless yourselves," whispered the priest. Some said the words out loud. The bolt was drawn back, the door opened and Darach Mor and Sean Pheggy darkened the doorway. They looked around with wonder and could not understand what had "In the name of the Father" to do with hide-and-go-seek.

"What's going on here at all?" asked Sean.

"Can't you see?" replied Pat, as the Rover was blindfolding him with the former vestment.

"We are playing games," shouted the house, rushing here and there, nearly knocking Darach down.

"Playing games, indeed!" sneered Sean, glaring at the Rover. "What brought you here, silly?"

"My two feet," replied the Rover, dancing a few steps of a reel. Then the house emptied.

Soon word got around and the whole village turned against us for our sinful act. Only the Rover remained our friend.

The Rover mended boots and wove baskets and skibs free for the neighbors. He had worked before the mast and sailed the Seven Seas. Had he been lucky in his roving life, he might never have come back to settle again in the old cottage by the sea where his ancestors had lived and died.

The Rover had served his time as an apprentice to a boatwright. When he had the trade learned, he started to build a pucan in a garden near the sea. Just as he began to lay the skin on the frame, a black bull came over from the next holding and, while scratching himself, stuck his head between two ribs of the boat. The beast made frantic but futile efforts to free himself, for the earth was trampled. The owner of the dead animal, Sean Mor, demanded damages from the Rover. The latter refused, saying that the bull had no right-of-way there. Sean brought him to court, claiming that the builder made a trap for the animal. The judge favored Sean, making out that the boatwright was a rebel against British rule. That misfortune put the Rover on the high seas.

One morning I was up with the chirp of the sparrow to help the Rover in his garden. It was a fine morning with a cloudless sky, the bay as smooth as a pane of glass as I trudged down the lane with a small spade on my shoulder. A lone rabbit sat on her haunches inside the wall, while another came over from the far hedge. They began to frolic, but there was no time to watch them. I had to dig the clay in the furrows as the Rover spread it on the ridges with a shovel.

"The young stalks are peeping through the skin of the soil, small pity the frost would show them," said I, scraping the sand off my spade with a scallop shell.

"True for you, Jimeen. Let's rest a while for the day is long," he suggested, sticking his shovel in the furrow and walking over to a green hillock. "The flax garden is ready to be molded and the weeds are coming up ahead of the potato stalks, but a good coat of mold will smother the dirt."

"Why is it called the flax garden?" I asked.

"Because flax used to grow in it long ago."

"How was the flax planted?"

"Old Coilin is the boy who could tell you all about that."

"He is a wonderful storyteller no doubt, but you visited strange lands and saw wonders galore that he never knew."

"True, a chara, but he who never left home is far more contented."

"Go on with you, man. What a noble thing to see the big world! That is what I'll do when I grow up so that I'll be rich."

"Mo lein!* There is none so unhappy as the man of wealth, for the money is his god and the more he has the more he wants. I heard a little story when I was young like you. Listen, a chara, and learn. Long ago there lived an Irish chief who was very rich, yet he was most unhappy and found no solace whatsoever in life. At last he sent for the wise old man. 'Ah, my faithful seer, I don't know in the world what ails me, but I'll find death in a short time unless I be cured. Musha, Druid of my heart who knows many things, can you give me some advice?'

" 'Well, my dear master, it is myself who knows that

* *Mo lein:* alas, my woe

you are ill, but you can and will grow well again if you follow my counsel. And here it is: Search your whole kingdom, find the happiest man there and wear his shirt next to your skin for three days and three nights. At the end of that time let me know how you feel!' "

"Sure, that was simple," I interrupted, trying to shoo away a bee that was zigzagging and humming in my face.

"Let the story spin on and you'll find out. This rich chief would trust his very soul with the Druid. Therefore, he ordered his clansmen to beat the four roads of Eire and search high and low. At long last when the space of time was nearly up——"

"What space of time?" asked I in surprise and watching a colony of ants marching single file with tiny twigs and vanishing into a little mound.

"Pardon me, but I forgot to tell you at first that the chief and the Druid had a gentlemen's agreement on a period of time to find the happy one. This period was drawing to a close now, so the clansmen sat down on a green hillside to rest, and they heard a fine song in the distance. They ran to the location and hid behind a rock to watch the singer. While they gazed secretly, this happy mortal sang, danced and somersaulted outside his own little hut. Hearing his merry laughter and finding him so gay and light-hearted, they knew well that here was the man they were looking for. But the storyteller did not say what happened to the chief because this contented merry man had only a rag on to cover his shame, and no kind of a shirt at all."

"Then it is not known whether the chief got well or not," said I, rising up and walking over to my spade in the furrow.

"A good lesson could be learned from it," smiled the

Rover, grasping his shovel. "It proves that riches are not everything in this world, and nobody can take any to the next."

"Very true," I agreed, beginning again to dig the mold.

"Look at the school of sea pigs diving outside the Point. That is a sure sign the pollacks are in from the Atlantic," he called out as he gazed out to sea.

Soon we had the field molded so that if Jack Frost should come like a thief in the night he could do no damage. Then the Rover lay stretched at his ease on the hill over the Oar Inlet. The sea to the west looked like a sheet of glass. The sky darkened and wisps of gray mist were joining to cap a sharp Beola peak to the northeast.

"Many is the day," said he to himself, "has gone by since I began to know the sea and I lying on this spot among the golden-blossomed furze. The fragrance of sweet clover was wafted to me by the wind from the glen. Those were happy carefree days. With my mind's eye I could see the love of my heart even on an empty cockleshell sailing along and the wind blowing through her golden hair. One must be young to see the beauty of the sea. Yet, like a maid, many are her moods. I often watched the dark green ridges one after another, their tops curling into snowy manes crashing in against the rocky shore with a thunderous roar, hurling spray and foam up to strike the clouds.

"Mo lein! Those pleasant days have passed forever when the hot blood gushed through my veins and I boiling over with vigor and courage. The shore of yon small isle looks gloomy now, but there was another day! That lovely day in June long ago when my love and I were full of joy going to pick some duilisg. We sailed in with a light wind from the west and landed on Duck Island and strolled along to the south shore where the sweet duilisg grew. On our way back with the basket full, my colleen slipped and cut her knee.

" 'Brighid, a stór, do not cry,' I whispered, kissing her tears away. I found a healing herb in the long grass, chewed and applied it to the cut, tore a strip from my shirt and wound it around her knee. On touching her soft skin, hot glows ran through me and the drop that lay asleep in my toe rushed to the roots of my hair. My arm stole around her waist and I pulled her gently toward me.

"It was a grand day with a soft warmth from the sun. The bay to the east was rippled by straying little breezes and a golden path led away to the westering sun. To the south lay Aranmor almost blotted out by a purple heat-haze. The humming of the bees came to us from the glen: 'Come along, a stór, and we might find some honey,' said I caressingly. We rummaged in the soft yellow moss of the valley but found none, so we sat down by the wall again. I put my arm around her and drew her head gently over, kissing her again and again until she silently gave me one back which melted my whole soul into ecstasy. We did not say anything for so long, nor did we feel the time passing, looking on the scene before us with half-closed eyes: yellow and white flowers peeping above the thick green grass; the lapping of the ebb tide on the shore interwoven with the crying of gulls coming to us; the humming of the bees growing louder as they flitted from flower to flower, a white clover blossom growing in a slit at the foot of the sea rod-laden wall and a yellow bee hovering over it. Love of my heart lay asleep by my side. I stretched out on the lush grass to watch the tiny wisps of sheep shearing moving slowly across the dome of heaven and to listen to the croon of the sea as the tide flowed in. Not a care or a worry in the whole wide world had we, but pleasure and happiness.

"The fresh wind carrying the same sea-salt tang as of old is coming again to me now from the heaving bosom of the Atlantic. The light mist is planting crystal drops on the purple heather before my eyes, but the sun will soon shine to soak it up."

The Rover rose to his standing, yawned and stretched himself. "Was I dreaming, or what has come over me at all?" he mumbled, tucking the corners of his bawneen under his multicolored girdle and glancing down at his gray homespun trousers to make sure that he was himself. "My bitter woe!" he mused, "but life is queer and no tongue can tell what time any of us will be called home. My own neighbor will sadly say some night or day: 'Poor Rover himself, after all he had traveled and seen, hoisted his sails at the turn of the tide for some port unknown; the blessing of dear God be with him.'"

※

"Get out of your daydreaming," my father's voice startled me. "Eat up your breakfast, for you are to go out to the post office and mail a letter and twelve pounds to Kinneen, Galway, for a few rolls of tobacco. Your brother and I will sail out to the bank."

Through the free play of my mind the plan to run away had been born and nursed. What better time than now? I put on my new homespun gray trousers and a pair of hobnailed boots. On the way to the post office, I changed the figures in the letter from twelve to nine, placing the three pounds in an inside pocket along with some silver change. I bought a money order for nine pounds and put it inside the letter. The post office clerk asked if I would take some letters for the village.

"I wish to visit the church first. Good day to you, miss."

"Oh, but you'll be back again," she smiled smartly.

The railroad station was fifteen miles away and I was never there before. But I knew one would not get lost following the telegraph poles that stood along the road. "A thousand goodbyes to the old life that I'm leaving behind, and céad míle fáilte before the new life which lies ahead," said I to myself, as I made the sign of the Cross and started to shorten the dusty white road alone.

On reaching the fifth milestone from my home, whom should I meet but Festy, the mountaineer.

"God bless you," he saluted, standing in the middle of the road and looking me straight in the eye.

"God and Mary bless yourself," I answered, looking down at my boots.

The cow, who from past experience knew well that her master would be in no hurry, wandered over to eat the grass on the side.

"Where are you bound for now, Jimeen?" he asked, taking off his caubeen and brushing back his thick reddish hair with his palm.

"Up to the mountain for the black heifer," I lied, a quiver in my voice.

"I thought you had sold that one to Colm Joyce," stroking his long reddish beard.

"We did, of course. But we have exchanged the yellow bull for her. He needs the mountain grass, for he was wasting away. And the heifer needs the shore. I must be on my way as it is growing late," glancing at the sun. "Good day to you, Festy."

"May your road prosper with you, Jimeen. I am on my way to the Island with the cow. I'll see you tonight with the help of God. Out of this with you, Speckles," swinging his shillelagh at the animal.

"Carts loaded with merchandise will be coming back from the railroad station this evening and the drivers might even persuade me to return home," thought I to myself.

The hills to the east were veiled in a gossamer haze. It might be wiser to leave the road to the devil and take the shortcut through the mountains. I crossed over the ditch, made my way to the top of a hill and hurried down the cheek of it waist deep in purple heather until reaching a level moor with rushes galore. "It is not possible for it to be soft this time of year," said I, glancing over at the foot of the mountain on the far side.

But as I advanced the marsh grew softer and the water came oozing over the top of my boots. Gladness came over me seeing a green mound dotted with red, amber and white plants. Ah, but my heart jumped to my mouth when it started to quiver under me like a huge feather bed. "Oh, Mhuirre, Mhuirre, Virgin Mary, help me," I cried. My prayer was answered, for I crawled back to safety on hands and knees. My soul from the devil but I was nearly swallowed alive in that belly of muddy water. What an innocent looking quagmire!

As I sat down on the heath to squeeze the water out of my stockings, the shrill sound of a whistle startled me. "Faith, but I have missed her," I moaned, watching the black ribbon of smoke from the train over the top of the hill. I was downhearted, tired and hungry. What could the matter be at all? I rose to my standing and began to shorten the way through a pass. Tired enough of the heather and furze was I when I walked into the railroad station at Recess.

"Will it be long now until the next train leaves for Galway?" I inquired.

The rosy-faced guard glanced at me from under his horn-peaked cap. "Four hours," answered he.

"Is there any place near where one could find a mouthful?"

"One mile that road to the north," indicating with his hand.

"Can I be back in time before the train leaves?"

"What train? It won't take you half an hour, and you have four hours to wait. Indeed, a chara, but the thirst of the world is on myself for I had some salted cod for my dinner."

I took to the road and ran, for I put no trust in the train.

In a short time, I reached a small pub at the foot of a hill. I ordered a pint of porter and a few slices of bread and had my meal which I needed. I also bought a pint of poteen for myself and two bottles of Guinness's stout for the guard. The porter and bread satisfied me, and I was light as a bird hurrying along through clouds of white dust raised from the road by the wind. The rye patches on the side of the road glistened and the leaves of the blackberry bushes stirred faintly. A flock of swallows skimmed low over a lake and the sound of carts could be heard in the distance. "Cuckoo, cuckoo, cuckoo," and there was herself perched on the gable end of a ruined church facing the southwest. "Am I to go back home again?" I muttered. The bird thought so.

I was back in the station in half an hour.

"You are a fine generous boy, God bless you," smiled the guard when I handed him the stout. "Where did you come from? Is it any harm to ask?"

"From the Island of Muighinis. I'm the son of Colm James."

"Faith, but I know him well. A fine honest man. To be sure, it is not from the sun and wind you got your fine generous nature. Where are you going now, a chara?"

Being so amiable himself, I let full rein with my tongue.

"You go back home again," he scolded. "You should never leave home without your parents' consent, for you might never see them again."

I handed him the flask of poteen to stop his tongue. He went deep in the pint as well as in the talk. Indeed, I needed a swallow myself, for I was on the edge of breaking down.

"I was only joking with you, my friend, I am only going as far as Galway to work the hooker back with my uncle because his boatman left him right there and eloped with a young girl over to Scotland. It was his story I had in mind to tell you but put myself in his place."

"Then where is your colleen?" he laughed. "But who would ever think that any man with a spark of sense in his head would leave a boat and his comrade for a slip of a girl!"

"Uh, excuse me, but I'd better buy my ticket now before the train comes in."

"You should be in Galway about ten o'clock tonight," he said, handing me the ticket. "This train will stop at many small stations along the way. Anyone will know the big city."

In a short time the train rumbled in and stretched along-side the platform with a clanking noise. "All aboard," shouted the guard. In a moment the train started to cough and squeak as she moved out. I put my head out through a window. Due to the curve in the tracks, I could see the whole length of the train crawling along. How in the world can the front part pull all those huge heavy boxes? asked I of myself. But once she took the curve out of her side, she sped quickly along between the sharp peaked hills. A river ran swiftly down a slope, roared wooly-white over a waterfall, flowed smoothly through a ravine, and stopped at last to keep company with a silvery lake in the glen. Just now we were coming to a village of thatched white-washed cottages nestled in the lap of a hill. Men working in the fields leaned on their spade handles to watch the train go by. Not one of them I knew.

A narrow passage loomed ahead. "Arrah, how in the world can she go through that slit?" I asked myself, stretch-ing out my neck to see better. A man at the window in front of me drew in his head quickly. But with the hurry pulling myself in, I fell in the lap of the lady next to me who smiled kindly. Gladness was on me that I had not lost my head when I saw the dark face of the bold rock so near as the train whizzed through the tunnel.

The train stopped at a station and there was a stir among the passengers. Some were getting off. I got off, too. "An e seo Gaillimh?"* I asked a well-dressed man carrying a valise in one hand and a cane in the other. He only stared at me. A bawneen-clad lad shouted, in the Gaelic, "You go right back into that train again. Hurry now. This is Uachtar Ard, and you are not half the way to Galway yet."

At long last the train rumbled into the big city itself. What a lovely sight to behold. Thousands of lights flickering and shining all over, yet I felt sad and lonely. Nor could I take the flask of poteen out as four peelers guarding a handcuffed rebel were sitting nearby. If they found the poteen on me, it might mean a year in an English prison.

When I stepped off the train, people were rushing here and there. Myself stood still lest I be knocked down. A fair-haired boy passing looked at me curiously.

"Where could I find a lodging for the night?" I asked him.

"Come along with me," he smiled.

We walked along through narrow crooked streets. I offered him a drink out of the flask. We went into a barroom and had a pint of porter each. After strolling along for a while, my guide said, "Here is the lodging house now."

"Thank you very much," handing him a florin and stepping inside where a maid showed me to my room. It was myself that could not find a wink of sleep that night, turning from side to side and full of loneliness, thinking about my people at home.

* *An e seo Gaillimh:* Is this Galway?

Early next morning I rose to make my way to the docks with the name of an Island nobby, Fagabealach (meaning get out of the way) on the breast of my knitted blue gansey for all to read.

The dock looked like a forest of bare pines with the masts of boats and ships. A three-masted vessel caught my eye; *Santa Maria* in white letters on her black stern. Several wild-looking bearded men were playing cards and arguing in loud voices on the deck.

"Would you have need of a boy?" asked I, when a man, who happened to be the mate, turned around.

"Well," he replied, taking the pipe out of his mouth and looking me up and down with half-shut eyes. "Have you any knowledge of the sea?"

"I know the sea very well," laying my finger on the green script on the breast of my gansey as if that were enough.

"One pound a month and your food. Come down in the cabin to sign the Articles," he ordered, taking off his cap.

An old Boatman from Conamara sitting on a rope post was eyeing me with a frown.

"I needs must go now and find my bag, but I'll be back in a jiffy," I told the mate of the ship.

"What were you doing on that ship?" the old Boatman asked me.

"I found a job on her as a cabin boy," I replied.

"You are a big fool."

"What can the matter be? Is it bad?"

"You know not what you are in for. You must go aloft taking in and shortening sails. Delph will be cracked on the top of your head. But pay me no mind. An advice bought is of more value than two free," he shrugged, walking away from me.

To drown my sorrows I strolled into O'Flaherty's pub

on the docks and ordered a pint of porter. I put my hand into my trouser pocket. My heart went pitter-patter and my mouth went dry as I searched my other pockets. All in vain. Then I remembered hiding the bills under my pillow the night before for fear I'd be robbed while I slept.

I turned on my heel and hurried up through the Spanish Archway, only to be stopped by three lads, who challenged me.

"Where is your hurry?" they shouted. "A bog trotter from the country is lost. What is that writing on the breast of your gansey? You think everyone will leave your way? Do you now?"

"It is the name of a nobby," I said politely.

A red-headed fat boy drew a line in the dust of the street with his dirty big toe. "I dare you to pass this line," he jeered.

It was hard for me to take this dare, but there was no time to argue. I rushed at him, turned sharply and, being a fast runner, left the lads far behind. On reaching my lodging place, I ran up the stairs and into the room. A woman was putting feathers in the bed. She screamed and threw a bag of feathers at me. A heavy set man ran up the flight of stairs and stopped in the doorway on seeing the feathers.

"You thief," he roared grabbing me by the shoulder.

"I am no thief," I gasped. "I put three pounds under my pillow here last night."

The man eyed me closely and asked, "Where did you come from?"

"I came in on the train last night from the West."

"Perhaps you stayed in the lodging house next door. Come along with me, and we shall see."

Sure enough, it was the next house and the three notes

were still there under the pillow, which made me very
happy.

It was not down to the ship I went. For one thing I did
not like the wild-looking crew, and the warning words
of the Conamara Boatman also discouraged me. Scotland
came to my mind now, and I directed my footsteps toward
the railroad station.

I had not gotten far through this narrow street when I
saw a mass of people rushing toward me. I tried to push my
way through but was carried backward by the surge of
human tide. At long last, I reached the station by a side
street just as the Dublin train was moving out from the
platform. I have missed it again! What will I do now?

In about half an hour the morning train came in from the
West. There was the same rush and hurry as on the pre-
vious night, with people running here and there. Uniform
caps pushing hand trucks loaded with bags and parcels
and making a power of noise on the concrete. What is all
this hurry for, I wonder? Surely the tide is not ebbing
away from anybody here.

My eyes opened wide with the wonder, for coming
through the crowd toward me was my father. There was
the quick change in my thoughts, but I did not know what
to say or do.

"What came over you at all, Jimeen?" he asked gently.
"Why didn't you let us know, and we would have you
ready for America. Your mother is near dead with the
grief after you. Festy, the mountaineer, told us that he had
met you on the road. Here's the money now to pay your
way to the United States," taking a roll of bank notes from
his pocket.

My tongue stuck to the roof of my mouth and a lump

came in my throat. Tears filled my eyes. No word at all could I say.

"Come along, son," smiled Daida, putting his arm around my shoulder. "We'll see the big city together."

As we strolled along, he told me the history of the old walls, churches, moats and castles built by the Spaniards centuries ago when Galway was young. "And that now is Lynch's Castle. Do you see the sign of the crossbones at that long window near the top," pointing with his finger. "That is the window from where Mayor Lynch hung his one and only son."

Tilting my head back, I read the harsh inscription underneath the window: "This ancient memorial of the stern and unbending justice of the chief magistrate of this City, James Lynch Fitz Stephens, elected Mayor A.D. 1493, who condemned and executed his own guilty son Walter on this spot."

"Why did he do that?" asked I.

"Because the son killed a Spanish boy who was a guest in their home. It seems that young Lynch became jealous of the Spaniard thinking his own sweetheart was falling in love with him."

We went into an inn to have our meal. Afterward we strolled down to the docks. My heart went pitter-patter on seeing the ship, *Santa Maria*, at anchor out on the roads. Hookers and nobbies galore were lined alongside the docks, and the boatmen were stripped to their shirts loading bags and boxes.

"God bless the work," my father saluted.

"God and Mary bless yourself, Colm," replied Eamonn O'Maille, a husky boatman from Conamara we knew well. "Did you come in the hooker for a cargo?"

"Not at all," smiled my father, sitting on a rope post. "I took this trip on the train to have a look at the beautiful scenery through the Twelve Bens and——"

Myself wandered away down the docks to have a look around. There was not a breath of air nor a wisp of cloud in the blue sky above. The sunbeams danced on the wet rocks bared by the ebbing tide. A ribbon of black smoke rose from the funnel of a hooker nearby. Further out in the bay was a small island with a whitewashed lighthouse on its humped back and the black hull of a wrecked vessel lying high and dry on its rocky shore. The *Cladach Gleotogs*, three sailing boats of seven ton, were coming back after the night's fishing, and the crews were singing and rowing up against the current in the mouth of the Corrib River.

"Come along, Jimeen," my father called, beckoning with his hand and also inviting four of the boatmen to come along. We saluted into Michael Walsh's pub on High Street, he who was murdered many years afterward by the English Black and Tans, may dear God have mercy on his soul. In a short time the boatmen were pleasantly lit and arguing about fast-sailing boats and famous regattas, Daida handed me a silver crown and told me to spend it.

"Be sure now and come back, little man," smiled Eamonn, adding half a crown in my hand.

I walked up Shop Street as light as a starling, jingling the silver coins with the tips of my fingers until I felt a tap on my shoulder. I turned around quickly and came face to face with a thin scrawny man.

"I don't know you at all," said I dryly.

"Ah, don't let that make you a bit strange. Folks do meet but the hills and mountains never. Indeed, I am your friend, but of course you were too young when I was back to remember me now. Mo lein! son," tilting his head back and putting a bold cheek on himself. "A thousand good-byes to the milk of the cow that was warm. Many is the merry night I spent back there."

"You were back in Muighinis then?" I exclaimed, and we walked side by side up the street, myself taking long steps to match his speed.

"Arrah, how is your father? He was an able man on the sea and a kindhearted soul, too. Have ye all the sheep yet, or is the little bootmaker still there?" feeling my trousers and looking down at my boots. He did not mind whether I answered or not.

"Well, a stór, I have the thing here now for you. Don't you do a bit of writing?"

"I write a little in the Gaelic," I replied, wondering how did he know.

"Here it is, son, and a thing of beauty forever," taking a fountain pen out of a narrow little box and handing it to me. "You can see for yourself the price written on the lid. How much does it say, son?" pointing his finger at the script.

"Ten shillings. Can it write good?"

"Write, a stór? It can write by itself almost, but try it yourself——" handing me a bit of paper.

"It can write fine," smiled I, for I was so eager to have it. "How much do you want for it?"

"Are you sure now that you need such a fine pen? If you do, it won't be ten shillings nor nine either. I'd be ashamed to ask eight of you, son of your mother. Give me your hand, son of an honest father. I'll make one word with you: three half-crowns," giving a gentle squeeze to my hand.

While I was counting the change, he was fixing the pen in the box. I handed him the money.

"Put the box in your pocket right now, son, for one of those lads idling around might snatch it out of your hand. Faith, you can't trust anyone in the big town; all are schemers of one kind or another."

I put the little red box into my pocket and himself turned around the corner as silently as a cat.

Daida and his comrades were still in the tavern when I returned. "You couldn't have the town bought since," laughed Eamonn, handing me a glass of lemonade.

"Well," smiled I, taking the box out of my pocket, "I spent seven and sixpence for a fountain pen that was worth ten shillings. See it marked right here on the lid. I just got a good bargain from a very friendly fellow," taking it out as the others looked on. My eyes nearly popped out of my head with the wonder and I felt a kind of sick: the box was empty!

On our way down to the docks, Daida invited his friends into Martin Ashe's pub to have deoch an dorais. The daughter of the house, a fine girl, handed me a paper full of sweets. While glancing shyly at her pleasing ready smile and feeling the sweetness of the candy under my tooth, the misery about the fountain pen vanished.

That evening Daida and myself took the train for the West. The weariness of the world was on me trying to keep my eyes open, listening to my father telling me the names of the towns we were passing. At last his voice and the chatter of the wheels on the rails mingled and faded away in the distance.

Sailing the wide open sea on board the Argentine barque, *Santa Maria*, on a voyage to South America. Storms and high seas. . . . In the smelly cabin washing dishes, thrown back and forth by the lurching and tossing. "All hands on deck," shouts the mate. A plate breaks in smithereens on the top of my head, blood is running down my face and I am scared. I am shivering climbing up a swaying rope ladder, sharp hailstones cut my face and I crawling out on the yard to furl the canvas that is flapping wildly. A flash of lightning and wonder of the world! Festy with his long beard flowing in the wind and he on the ladder under me, shouting, "Ah, you rogue, why did you say you'd be home tonight? Your people are looking for you every-where and——"

A sudden gust of wind blows the sail free from the yard. I hang on for dear life flying through space like a bird. I have a drowning man's grip on the sail. A dangling rope winds around my neck from the antics of a twister. Light-ning flashes on the white-maned rolling swells underneath. "God and Mary save me," I screamed and woke up. Some of the passengers were laughing. "You must have been in terrible danger," said Daida. The cold sweat was coming out through my face, yet happiness galore was on me to hear the shrill whistle and the coughing of the train as it rumbled into Recess Station.

That same evening we rode home from the station in a jaunting car. Our dog, Watch, and my sisters and brothers met me in the garden west of the house and greeted me warmly. The dog ran toward me, wagging his tail and jumping up trying to kiss my face. My sisters, Mairin and Barbara, were very happy that I was back home again, and I started right away to tell them all about the big city. My mother wept tears of joy and kissed me again and again. "Faraway hills look green, a stór, but there is no place like home," she smiled.

A cruiskeen of poteen stood on the table and the neighbors were sitting around in the kitchen, happy and singing Gaelic songs to honor my homecoming.

"Céad míle fáilte before you," laughed Old Paudeen, shaking my hand. "My soul from the devil but you have a drop of brave blood in you, not like those who are stuck in the ashes and pass away in the end just the same. Ah, if I were young again, I'd act much different than I did."

Daida found the glasses and filled them.

"It surely holds the beads," smiled Mickileen Liam, raising his glass.

"Here is health to ye all and slainte* Jimeen, too, for we would not find this treat of mountain dew tonight, only for his homecoming," exclaimed Martin O'Cooney as he shook my hand warmly and tossed back his glass.

* *slainte:* health

On the Island a holiday is made to honor the dead. No work at all is done until the burial is over. The Rover would come to make the coffin of white pine boards. The lonesome sound of his hammer could be heard far from where he was working. A score of men dressed in their homespuns idled around to watch him measure, saw, plane and build. Sad looks were on their faces as they chatted in low tones, the blue knitted caps pulled down over their foreheads. Even the black hornless cows in the next garden lowed sadly as they listened to the hammer driving home the nails.

"Are you going to the wake?" asked Pat Bartly of myself one evening.

"Just wait a minute," said I. Hurrying into our house to find a pinch of salt, I put a grain of it under my tooth, a grain in my pocket and pitched the rest over my left shoulder into the fire.

The wakehouse was full and you could not see your outstretched hand with all the tobacco smoke. We threaded our way to where the corpse was laid-out on the board, knelt and blessed ourselves. Una's long face on the empty herring barrel, which stood under her head because the board was too short, frightened me. Pat was scared, too, and he nearly knocked me down with the hurry when we rose from our knees. The house was very quiet save for the cricket that chirped in the hob. Darach Mor and Luke Paudeen were at a table cutting tobacco, filling clay pipes and handing them around.

"The blessing of dear God be with her soul," one would whisper when handed a pipe. "Ah, but we all must come to this."

The dark of the night had begun to mingle with the light of the day, just as the pucan landed at the pier. No sooner had the ten-gallon poteen keg come in through the doorway than the quietness of the moment before vanished. Only the cheerful cricket kept on as he was. Luke and Mickileen Liam found pitchers and glasses to serve the mountain dew around.

"It is a good drop," smiled O'Cooney, holding the glass between his eye and the lamp on the wall.

"It sure holds the beads," added Martin son-of-Anna. "A bad drop never came from Inisbarachain."

"May the Lord have mercy on her soul and all the souls of the faithful departed," prayed the stocky little bootmaker when he was handed his glass.

Little Nan and Maire Sally were now busy preparing a meal. Because of the small kitchen, a couple of the neighbors went out to ready the barn. Planks were stretched by the walls with flat stones under their ends. In a short time soda bread, butter and mugs of tea were set in the regular order on the tables. When one group had eaten, another pulled in.

"May God not weaken you, Coilin, and tell us a story to shorten the tail of the night," asked Darach Mor respectfully.

"Toss this thimbleful back, a chara, and let us have the story," added Mickileen Liam.

"Well, as ye are so hard on me," Coilin smiled, and he a wee bit softened by the barley juice, "I'll spin ye one about the time long, long ago when the Son of God wandered on this earth teaching the people, raising the dead and making wine out of water."

"Making wine out of water!" O'Cooney repeated. "Arrah, some people make poteen out of water nowadays."

"Silence," retorted the bootmaker, glaring at O'Cooney. "Christ made wine out of pure water at a wedding in the Holy Land and you compare that with the worldly distillers."

"Stillers, my eye! 'Twas a shebeen* man where I bought a pint and 'twas all water but the smell," exclaimed O'Cooney, slapping his palm on the bootmaker's knee.

"Pardon me, a chara, but you did hit the nail on the head. Indeed, some shebeeners baptize the poteen freely," agreed the bootmaker.

"Go ahead with the story, Coilin.

Coilin coughed to clear his throat and began. "It was a long, long time ago and if we were in it then, we would not be here now," crossing his legs, taking off his beret and leaning back in the chair. "Peter and James were partners in a fine fishing boat much the same as partners are in boats nowadays. John and Thomas made kelp on the shore of the Holy Land just as we ourselves do now on the south shore. Christ Himself was a great carpenter and boat builder. From all the evidence we have He was a master builder as well as a master teacher. One fine day in the summer, He was teaching a large crowd down near the shore of Galilee. Many of His listeners had come from afar and had been fasting for a few days.

" 'We are half dead with the hunger, Teacher!' they cried, 'and nothing at all to eat in this wild part of the country.'

* *shebeen:* saloon

" 'Have a little patience my friends,' replied the Teacher calmly, 'until I find out if that boat at anchor in the bay has any fish today,' walking down to the shore.

"The crowd expected Him to call out to the fishermen. But great was their surprise on seeing their Teacher walk out on the sea toward the boat.

"Peter, the captain who had his head stuck up in the companionway smoking his pipe, could hardly believe his eyes. The clay dudeen fell out of his mouth and was broken in smithereens. 'Come up quick,' he shouted down to the crew, 'until ye see the wonder of wonders—a man walking on the water!'

" 'He might be the great Teacher that people come from far and near to see and hear,' said one.

" 'Whoever He is he has done a wonderful deed that will go down in history yet,' added a scrawny red-headed member of the crew, taking paper and pencil out of his pocket.

" 'Have ye much fish today, God bless ye?' asked Christ, laying His hand on the rail.

"There was a short pause, for all were leaned over the rail peering sharply trying to see had He a cork under His feet.

" 'Not much,' Peter replied, 'but all we have is Yours,' putting five haddocks on a string.

" 'Our friends yonder,' pointing to the shore, 'are weak with the hunger and have no patience anymore.'

" 'We have some bread in the cabin,' said Peter, making a sign to Red to bring them up. 'Musha, how can You walk on the sea?'

" 'You can, too, if you have faith. Come along and help me carry the bread ashore. You'll have time galore before you sail out to sea,' swinging the string of fish on His left shoulder.

"Peter looked Him in the face and a strong feeling of courage came to him. 'Yes, Master,' he replied, picking up the bag of bread.

"Christ and Peter made toward the shore, while Red wrote on and said in a confident tone: 'This is as it should be, it was in the prophecy.' As the two walked on, the crew leaned on the rail watching them. A roving wisp of wind that didn't disturb the sleepy air rippled the surface. Peter lifted his feet with care lest he'd splash any water on his Master's robe. He started to think of the great depth under his feet and it seemed to him that a shark lay lurking under the surface. Great fear seized him and he began to sink.

" 'Master, save me,' he cried, throwing his hands in the air.

"The Master gave him His hand as he was sinking, saying, 'What can the matter be?'

" 'Kind Master, didn't you see the shark who was about to swallow me?' Peter mumbled.

" 'That was no shark at all but a tiny haddock,' pointing with His finger.

"Peter blushed to the roots of his hair. If his crew knew that such a coward was he, the best captain at sea, well— He pressed the Other on the shoulder and whispered, 'Never let this beside Your breath and I'll never lose faith in You again!'

"The Master smiled and stepped with Peter onto land.

"The multitude on shore knelt, then rose to their standing, bowed and gave three loud cheers. Five haddocks were cleaned and put in a pot on the fire. The bread was cut in thin slices. The people started to mill around grumbling as the hunger gnawed at their hearts, and the food was like a strawberry to a bull.

"With uplifted hands, the Master declared calmly, 'Food and drink for the multitude.'

"Instantly the plate of bread began to increase until it was as big as a small hill, and the pot of fish grew to the size of a boat and a spring of fresh water gushed out of the ground."

"Wasn't that a great miracle walking on the sea?" interrupted the Changeling. "Wet your lips, Coilin," as the Changeling served the mountain dew.

"Here's slainte to all and may God relieve the suffering souls in Purgatory," toasted Coilin, raising his glass.

"Well," broke in O'Cooney, when he had his tossed back, "I'd say myself that making a mountain out of a handful of bread and changing the old skillet into a boat were greater wonders than walking on the sea. Didn't you and me often see Tom son-of-John asleep on the water out in the bay, and he snoring so loud one fine day adrift with the ebb luring the gulls to where he lay."

"Hush," snapped the bootmaker, nodding at the storyteller.

"Where was I?" asked Coilin, scratching the back of his head.

"Where the fountain gushed," replied the bootmaker.

The narrator pushed back his thick hair with his palm. "Skipper Peter and a few of the lads began to whisper among themselves sneaking down to the shore. Peter wanted to show off—how he could walk on the sea, you know.

" 'Where are you going, Peter?' called the Master, without turning His head.

" 'Nowhere at all,' was Peter's reply."

"Then Peter told a lie," Darach Mor said gravely.

"Go on with you, that wasn't a real lie at all," grinned O'Cooney. "Maybe someone had a flask, and they were going behind the hillock to wet their throats, or perhaps someone wanted to open a button."

"Silence for the storyteller," snapped the bootmaker. "Go ahead, Coilin."

"Large as was the crowd, they couldn't finish the food. But when the congregation left, flocks of white gulls and black crows darkened the skies, hurrying to feast on the leavings. That now is the end of my story."

"Thank you very much, Coilin. It is nice how you have shortened the night and kept us awake," chorused the house.

"It is about time to say the Rosary," whispered the bootmaker, taking the beads out of his pocket and kneeling.

While the mourners recited the Rosary, the rooster crowed and flapped his wings three times, the geese in the yard honked and the donkey brayed. Something was moving around outside. When the house rose off their knees, a cruiskeen was filled out of the keg, so if evil spirits were outside some lively spirits were going around inside, too.

It was growing bright in the east now and some of the mourners were returning to their homes. Two keening women in their sixties with rosy faces and dark hair stood up—one had large grayish eyes dotted like a lark's egg and the other eyes as blue as the flax flower. They shuffled slowly over to the corpse and began to hum a lullaby, beating their palms together and swaying from side to side: "Una, you were the kind and generous one with love for all. You are sailing home to God in your fine boat of pine." Then raising their sorrowful voices together, "Una, a stór, have our beds ready for us there some day or night maybe. The ebb in the bay won't let us stay and many is the night and day we'll lie in the cold, cold clay and our tongues will taste no tay. Sure, it's the day that makes no lie, Una, we'll be with you bye and bye."

Then beating their palms together and wailing: "You are gone away from us Una, a stór, never will we see you any more at the gable end when the birdies sing at early morn."

They paused for a couple of minutes, and the house was in silence as they walked slowly over to their seats.

The third day of the wake was bright and sunshiny. Una had a large funeral. She had been a kind person, and there was poteen galore served, also refreshments. The coffin was carried for the first seven steps by four persons of the same surname. Who would shoulder the burden from then on made no difference.

The curate stepped forward to bless the grave. Two of the neighbors were down in the hole pitching up the dry white sand.

"I think she is deep enough," whispered Luke.

Red James agreed by throwing his shovel upon the bank. Both climbed up, brushing the sand off their clothes and bowing to the priest. The coffin was lowered into the six-foot hole by means of a rope.

"May the Lord have mercy on her soul," prayed the rosy-faced priest, putting a purple stole around his neck and saying the holy Latin prayers, then taking a shovel in his hands and pitching some sand down on the coffin.

On hearing the thudding sounds of sand on wood, the dead woman's kin began to weep. The keeners joined in swaying from side to side on their bare sturdy legs, stooping down shoulder to shoulder wailing a lament. "Ochone oh! Ochone a stór. In this vale of tears and sadness we'll never see you more," kneeling in a crouch, their heads touching the ground.

In a short time the hole was filled with sand. Stones and shells were carried from the shore nearby and spread on the grave. The curate and the people knelt and recited the prayers for the dead in Gaelic. Then they rose to their standing and started for home. The keeners were in the vanguard, jostling each other and laughing like children at play.

"Mo lein! How sad it is for those who pass away, and we all must come to it," sighed Old Coilin. "See the hurry that's on them now, leaving poor Una here alone with the dead. Ah, but man is only a shadow and life an empty dream," he sighed, drying his cheeks with the sleeve of his bawneen and walking slowly after his neighbors to the village of Meallruadh.

*

I often had heard Daida tell about the day he and Old Coilin were sailing from Galway in a hooker, on their way to the city to exchange their dulse and carrigeen for supplies. While sailing west by Castle Point, a sea serpent longer than the boat itself was seen lifting his head above the surface. Terrified men and women prayed and sprinkled holy water out into the ocean. Among the passengers was an individual named Flaherty, who had offended the priest of the parish. The Holy Father had cursed him from the altar one Sunday.

Some on board began to mutter that this wicked man was reason enough for the monster to appear, that he might chew a hole in the belly of the boat and drown them all.

On overhearing the talk, the sinner exclaimed, "I am right here and let him find me."

"Did ye hear what he said?" shouted one, looking around.

"Let's throw him overboard, or we'll all be in the belly of the monster soon," urged another, laying his hands on the poor man who began to scream. And before the more sensible could save him, Flaherty was pitched overboard into the ocean.

"Man overboard! Down with the helm!"

"Ease her up in the wind," ordered a member of the crew as he slackened the stays.

Daida, who was at the helm, sent the boat trembling up in the eye of the wind. A boatman coiled a rope and pitched the end deftly to the drowning man. All were peering over the side expecting to see the beast open his jaws and swallow the sinner. But the latter grabbed the rope, and all gave a hand pulling him in as the boat plunged ahead in the cheek of a mountainous swell. The rescued man shook a shower of water out of his clothes and stood on the deck shivering in a maze of confusion, not knowing whether to be grateful or angry at his erstwhile enemies.

"Well," smiled Coilin, looking Flaherty in the eye.

"You were innocent, sure enough, otherwise you would be in the other world now. How this reminds me of the time long ago when Jonah was swallowed by the whale."

"Arrah, Coilin, tell us the story about it," chorused several, wishing to create better feelings aboard.

"Indeed," the storyteller began, "Jonah wasn't guilty either. Here is how I heard it from my grandfather, may dear God be good to his soul.

"Jonah was on board a hooker loaded with villagers sailing west to see our team play football against the Clochronta boys. As we were rounding Ceann Reamhar, someone noticed a spout of water shooting high into the air, then a whale rising astern and following us. Fear showed on every face when the monster began to bump the bottom of the boat. Holy water was sprinkled and all aboard recited the Rosary. Soon a low frightened murmur was going on among the passengers, spelling out that Jonah was the cause of the monster's appearance since he had made the big blunder of digging new potatoes for a Druid by the light of the moon. At that time, you know, the Druids were shunned by good Christians.

"The excited mob was milling around now, shouting that Jonah should be thrown to the beast as a sacrifice. They grabbed the terror-stricken man and pitched him overboard. The hooker sailed on with a brisk breeze, leaving the poor soul far astern. Just as he was nearing the end of his struggle, the whale spied him.

" 'What happened to you?' asked the whale. You see, animals could talk then.

"It took some time before Jonah could speak, for his stomach was full of water.

" 'They pitched me overboard for no reason at all!' said he.

"Just then a shark appeared and started to grumble. 'What's the matter with you?' he asked the whale angrily, eyeing Jonah with a hungry look.

"The whale gulped and said with the tears rolling down his cheeks, 'The poor lad was drowning when I saved him.'

" 'But he is one of those evil men who catch us in nets and pitch sharp iron spears at us.' The shark edged closer and opened his mouth so wide that Jonah could see rows of pointy white teeth."

"It must be a miracle that poor Jonah lived through it out there alone on the deep," Sean Pheggy said.

The storyteller went on.

" 'Take off those heavy boots and I'll swallow you. You'll be safe in my stomach,' whispered the whale.

"Jonah took off his new hobnailed boots and let them down in the deep, though it went to his heart. His big friend swallowed him right away and dived out of sight. Now and again the kind animal used to come to the surface for air and Jonah got a share, too.

"One day Jonah was sitting on the back of the whale, trying to lure some fish by wiggling his toes in the water. By this means he caught an odd mackerel, which took the edge off his hunger. On coming to the surface this misty afternoon, he saw a little boat fishing a short distance away. Jonah knew that it was his mortal enemy the tailor, and

he would rather die than go aboard with him. The tailor
was standing in the prow letting slack with the mooring
rope. There was a small bundle lying on the stern-lockard.
The whale came astern and Jonah snatched the package,
which contained a loaf of bread, a bottle of milk and a
jackknife."

"That was a clever trick played on him," put in Mickileen Liam. "He was a tailor from the western island and
had a bad name in the Barony."

"The bream fisherman caught a glimpse of the hand
taking his lunch, and he rowed home in a fright," Old
Coilin went on. "He told the neighbors about seeing the
hand of a sea serpent. His friends winked at one another,
for they were sure that the tailor must have met a poteen
boat and had drunk too much mountain dew.

"One clear evening the whale surfaced. Jonah looked
around, hoping to see some friendly boat. He saw one all
right with a man standing in the bow, his uplifted arms
holding something that glistened in the bright sunshine.

" 'Dive quick,' Jonah shouted to the whale. 'A sharp
iron is poised ready to bury itself in your body.'

"He dived at once sick from the fright, he belched and
belched, broke wind and moaned.

" 'I'm near dead,' he whispered to his companion. 'I long
for my own kith and kin in the Arctic Sea. But I'll try for
the shore first that you might have a chance of saving yourself.'

"Jonah had been three days and three nights in the belly
of the whale, and he felt sorry for his kind friend who had
saved his life. On coming near the yellow strand of the
Island, the whale vomited. The rumbling stirred the sea
around in waves. Jonah was thrown out and floated ashore
on the vomit.

"Now the tailor who we mentioned before had taken a strong liking for Jonah's wife. When the sad news came that Jonah had fallen overboard going to the football game in Clochronta, the priest asked the congregation on the following Sunday to pray for his soul. Was the tailor not now free to marry the woman of his choice?"

"To be sure everyone in the parish knew about his bad behavior," spoke out Martin O'Cooney. "A born rogue and a deceiver, too. But strange as it may seem, the women desired his company."

"Indeed they always do," Coilin agreed. "But back to our story.

"Jonah, who was supposed to be drowned, came home one night. The trousers of gray homespun which were made for his legs were now on his back. Strings were tied around the leg bottoms and the whole filled in with ambergris. Bearing this heavy load on his back, he knocked on his own door but got no answer. If he had only had his boots on, he'd have kicked it in. He hurried to the bedroom window, rapped, shouted and at last smashed it. The rascal of a tailor who was inside with his wife sneaked out through the back door and ran all the way home in his pelt thinking it was Jonah's ghost. When our hero convinced his woman that he was himself, she hid the tailor's clothes under the bed and let him in.

"The news spread that Jonah had received five hundred pounds for the ambergris. It reached the landlord's ears, making him raging mad.

" 'That precious stuff came ashore on my estate, and according to the law of the land, it is mine,' said the landlord to Jonah.

" 'You can go to the devil,' replied the other.

"The tyrant lost no time but brought Jonah to court.

Not only did the poor man lose out, but he was sentenced to a year in prison for not reporting his find to the barrack. He didn't live long in the rotten English prison. His body was brought home to be waked and kept in three days and three nights as was the custom. Poteen, tobacco, pipes and food galore were served to the wakers. Indeed, he had a big funeral for he was well-liked in the parish. Stones were carried up from the shore and laid on the grave as was the custom then and still is. The tailor also gave a hand, picked out the heaviest lumps of granite he could carry and laid a score of them on the grave along with the rest.

"Strolling over to the widow, he whispered in her ear: 'May the Lord have mercy on his soul. He is lying at last in the dry white sand six feet deep; but if he can rise up from that heavy load, it will be one of the Seven Wonders!' And that's the end of my story," said Coilin, taking out his pipe and lighting it.

The former sinner, Flaherty, cheered up as he listened and began to look upon himself as akin to the Biblical Jonah. His persecutors had already shared with him their own dry garments, and they too looked upon him as a hero. They had a few bottles of poteen aboard and served them around.

"We are very, very sorry for our rash judgment on you, a chara," they said contritely as they clinked glasses. "And thank you very much, Coilin, for you have shortened the way nicely and cheered the boat. Here we are at Golam Head and near home," they chorused, shaking hands warmly with the storyteller.

*

Another fine storyteller was Old Paudeen, and as fine a fisherman as could be found in Conamara. So the time spent at sea along with him was as pleasant as it was profitable. I remember one fine day when we two were fishing for wrasse out at the wild rocks of Carriagemackan.

The wrasse, which lives among the red weed, sea moss and sea rod, is a beauty in brilliant colors. He might be darkish on the back, speckled with gold, white and green merging with the pale of the belly. A live one dangling on the hook is even more beautiful before he dies because of the vanishing iridescence on his coat of scales.

It was full tide, and due to the heat the fish had dropped their heads with some kind of laziness.

"Perhaps no other industry is as old as fishing," said Paudeen, taking out his pipe.

"I suppose there was no easier way in the far distant past to find a mouthful than by killing fish. I wonder if line-fishing is the oldest kind?" I asked.

"Nets were used in the time of Christ. But the old records tell us that the first fish was caught by bare hands. The idea for the hook came from the curved forefinger that the ancient inserted in the gills of the fish."

After hauling in the mooring-stone we rowed east until we were over a dappled bottom. As soon as the lines were out again, Paudeen said, "In the long ago, people galore lived on fish, not only near the shore but at lakes and rivers. Tree huts are still found in some lakes, showing that the fishermen of the time lived near the fish. A couple of years ago a giant canoe was found embedded in the bottom of Lough Corrib, and she was made out of the trunk of a tree."

"It must have taken a long time to fashion her out of the solid trunk," I laughed.

"That was thousands of years ago, Jimeen, and if we were in it then, we would not be here now and the fish would be left in peace," smiled Paudeen, pulling in a fat wrasse.

"The tide has turned, for the boat is swinging around," said I, putting a lugworm on my hook.

"Let's land on the rock and have a mouthful."

We rowed into an inlet and landed, gathered bits of wrack and made a fire. We cooked a fish and roasted a few potatoes. Soon we were enjoying a nice warm meal and strong tea afterward.

Paudeen took out his pipe and lit it. The midday sun was warm, and the dark flags around glowed with the heat. The big sea was like a huge pane of glass. From the west came long heavy swells, and the rays from the sun gleamed on their curved backs. The incoming tide licked the stones and played with long glossy-black ribbons of laminaria, pushing them into slits and sucking them out again.

"Do you see that rock down below?" asked my comrade, pointing the stem of his pipe. "That's where the schooner was wrecked many years ago."

"Were you not put in prison on account of her?" I asked.

"It was nearly the cause of my death, too. The turnkeys in Galway City near murdered me at the flogging post. I found a taste of Victorian justice, mind you. The curse of God on the British law."

"Was it not a strange place that she was driven ashore?" I asked.

"It was near the Christmas holidays at the time, and the Islanders were busy manuring their fields with red weed. This morning I rose up at cockcrow to try and find my share of the weed washed in. On finishing our work in the strand, we strolled up to a sand dune.

" 'Men!' shouted old Mickil and he running toward us from the south shore. 'A ship is high and dry on the Furoon Rocks. Come up to yon hillock,' pulling the nearest along by the sleeve, which happened to be myself.

"In no time at all six of us were bending our oars, and it wasn't long until we landed in that cove," said Paudeen, nodding his head toward the spot. "The schooner was lying on the shore and not a soul in her."

"Were the poor men lost?" I interrupted.

"Not at all. Though we didn't know it then," taking a drink of tea out of the can. "There she was with a gaping hole in her belly, with wrack scattered around which the next tide would sweep away. But we loaded our boat with it."

" 'Twas the sensible thing to do," I agreed.

"On arriving home that evening, we heard that the crew had landed safe that morning in Aillnabhron. The evening the schooner struck, you couldn't see your outstretched hand with the thick fog. She was tacking to the west with light wind and the strong ebb tide sucked her sideways on the reef. The crew at once began to pitch the cargo overboard, hoping that she would float. Soon they realized that every nail and bolt in her sleek black hull were to be her anchors forever. The skipper of the schooner told us the story one night afterward.

" 'Ah, there we were,' he began, 'And the scraping of her keel on the hard granite and the groans of her knees and timbers made us feel sick. Wind, we thought, would clear the mist and a good getaway would be much wiser than a poor stay. We began to build a raft out of planks. Though we had no idea where we were, we knew from the way the swells were rolling that the land was to the east. The raft was a strong one and we launched it over the side, loaded it with a firkin of butter, a bag of bread, a crate of crackers, a keg of water and some old clothes. We hoisted a bit of sail on an oar and took the last look on our fine boat before the mist enveloped her.

" 'All night long we were drifting with the tide. The fog cleared a little at the dawn of day, and were we happy to see land. In a short time we floated into a bay and were near solid earth. We managed with the help of an oar to guide the raft into an inlet, where it caught the edge of a sunken rock and part of our cargo slipped into the water. My comrade jumped in and carried the stuff up on the dry land. Then we knelt down and offered a prayer to God for bringing us safe. We didn't know yet in what part of the green land of Eire we were, but we made for a thatched whitewashed cottage at the foot of a hill. My partner was carrying a firkin of butter and myself a crate of crackers.

" 'God bless all here,' we saluted as one.

" 'God and Mary bless yourselves,' replied the man of the house.

" 'Musha, woman of the house, we didn't come empty-handed,' said I, laying the crate of crackers on the table.

" 'The man of the house brought in a cruiskeen and set it on the table, saying, "Ye do need a mouthful to warm ye up. Were ye in a boat?"

" 'We were, a chara, but our poor boat is a total wreck on a rocky reef off the Galway Coast. But God brought us safe on a raft to the cove down below.'

" 'The woman prayed, "The Lord save us from all harm. Myself had spent all night dreaming about boats, red weed, wrack and——"

" 'But the husband interrupted. "Dreams are bad luck before breakfast," he vouched, filling the glasses with poteen. "Put down a mouthful for the men."

" 'Here is good health.'

" 'The husband replied, "Good health to ye, men. Thank God that brought ye in safe from the sea."

" 'Let us run down and take up the other things,' said my comrade after we had eaten a good breakfast.

" 'On seeing the raft, the man of the house exclaimed, "By the Book, but it is a masterpiece."

" 'You can have it and welcome,' smiled I.

" 'He replied, "I'll pay you for it."

" 'Not at all, my friend.'

" 'While we lay in a dreamless sleep, the woman of the house dried our clothes.' And so the skipper of the schooner wrecked on the Furoon Reef concluded the story."

Old Paudeen gazed hard at the wild rock and his eyes were full of bitterness.

"Go ahead with your story, Paudeen," I urged gently.

Paudeen continued. "The news had spread about the men coming in from the sea on a raft. The peelers got word of it. The shipwrecked men were arrested as well as the man of the house for harboring them.

"Yes, Jimeen. I had been sound asleep that night long ago when a loud knock on the door woke me up.

" 'Who is there?' asked I.

"When the man shouted back in a strange tongue, I understood.

" 'Open the door in the name of Her Majesty, Queen Victoria, or we'll break it in.'

" 'Have a little patience,' I replied, lighting the lamp. I went to the door in my shirt and pulled the bolt. The dog rushed out, made a jump for the nearest peeler and tore the leg of his trousers. Eight saucer caps marched in armed with guns and bayonets, which glistened in the lamplight. They began to search and at last found two holy wax candles which are in every home for the use of the clergy when they give Extreme Unction to the sick. It would be as easy for me to bail out the bay as to say that I didn't find them on the schooner."

"Even if they didn't find anything," I interrupted, "they'd drop something and find it again. How often did the peelers hide a flask of poteen in a poor man's haystack and find it afterward so that the Islandman would be fined in court and imprisoned, too!"

"Very true," Paudeen agreed. "Anyway, the two candles so enraged them that they tore up the bed with the bayonets, broke the chairs and kicked the children. They put handcuffs on myself and marched me up the old road along with five others. On the long road to Galway City, they picked up many more rebels who had been fighting the British. If any of us fell back, he would find the taste of the whip from the peeler.

"The day of the assizes came at long last and we were tried. The peelers swore on the Book that we stole the property of Her Royal Highness, Queen Victoria, from a ship that was wrecked off the Galway Coast. The judge put on his black cap and sentenced each of us to six months of hard labor."

"It was a cruel law," I put in.

"Many is the honest man that was murdered in cold blood. When the peeler put his finger on you, the prison, convict ship, or the hemp rope would be your fate in the end. The turnkeys in the rotten Galway prison were a mean gang. One night I'll never forget until the last breath leaves my body. The icy wind was piercing me to the marrow, and when all was quiet I stole across the passage and lay down on the board beside one of my neighbors to keep a little warm."

" 'What are you up to now?' roared a turnkey, striking me with a whip again and again as I ran back to my cell. For a whole week after that I had to live on water and was also sentenced to twenty strokes of the cat-o'-nine-tails. I was tied to a post that had been hammered into God's earth. I turned my eyes upward to a patch of blue sky and whispered a prayer; I trembled when I saw the well-fed brute moving toward me and he cracking his whip. Mind you, but those floggers were well-paid in the service of the Empire. He raised his whip and struck me again and again as I stood there naked and helpless."

"Those posts were much like the ones in the old schools where children were tied for talking in the Gaelic," I reminded Paudeen.

"Both were used for the same purpose, to make the child as well as the man loyal to the Empire. The English lords and ladies, when they grew tired of hunting and carousing, watched those acts of cruelty in the prisons, yelling and clapping their hands. The brute finished his job on me by throwing a bucket of brine on the top of my head. I left a trail of blood as they dragged me back to the cell."

"It is a great wonder that you lived through it," I put in.

"Indeed, there were worse acts. The treadmill was an instrument of torture. If you missed your step on the pedal you'd be made a cripple for life. A hunchback prisoner made small stumps of a cable with an ax and pitched them to me to change into fluffy oakum with my bare hands. I saw a boy lose an eye one evening when a sliver flew from a stone he was breaking. Many is the day I put in myself breaking stones into small pieces, for one would have to do so many yards in a day.

"The cry of a poor fellow came to my ears one evening while he was tortured with the cat-o'-nine-tails by a flogger. It seems that an official found some large stones hidden in his heap to make it look big."

"And what did the prison do with all those things?"

"Sold them. It was dear the roadmender paid for the small stones and the ship chandler for the oakum. But to come to the end of my story, myself did suffer much on account of the Furoon schooner."

"God save the storyteller," I exclaimed. "See now how you have shortened the fine day. It must be time to be making sail."

While the fisherman's garden is broad and long, yet the yield is not often in proportion to the area. The kelpmaker is much in the same boat, for though he has shore galore, his income is poor due to the bad weather and rough seas.

The Islanders used to deal in our little shop. I can still see the fisherman walking in and saying to my father: "Could you give me a sack of flour, some tea, sugar and tobacco which I need now until my earnings come in. Next summer, with the help of the Lord, I'll have a thousand wrasse and pollack cured and saved, also a few score bags of carrigeen and duilisg."

He got the stuff then and afterward for the wrasse that was sleeping in his lair among the waving sea rods; the schools of mackerel, cod and pollack that were swimming in the ocean thousands of miles to the west; the lobsters hiding in the slits of the rocks, and the dark carrigeen still in its infancy. Also for the red weed and laminaria growing on the rocks away in the deep, which had to be cut and taken ashore, dried by the sun and burned into blue kelp.

The weed-burning season in the fall was a busy time in Conamara. As children we loved to play around and chase one another through the thick creamy smoke from the kiln, slanted low by the wind. In the afternoon the women brought tea and cake, maybe a bottle of poteen to nourish the burners.

Our neighbor, Red James, used often to give us a hand with the burning. He was a well-knit man with a long red beard and blue eyes. He claimed that he was a master burner. He would take off his blue knitted cap and spit on the iron of the kelp rack and push it into the glowing red hole in the kiln; put his ear to the end of the wooden handle with his right hand raised for silence. "Ha, ha," he'd whisper, going on one knee and putting a wise look on his face. "Musha, glory be to the Lord, I can hear the pure iodine in the burning weed escaping in flame and smoke up to the heavens—a thousand thanks be to God—hissing like a live thing in the bowels of the hot kiln."

"Let me listen in too," I begged, moving toward the handle of the kelp rack, nearly tripping him.

"Out of my way, you silly little fool. You have to spoil the whole blessed thing. Your soul from the devil, keep out. Hurry Jimeen, bring in an armful of weed from the stack, and may God bless you."

When I brought him the courlough he was in good humor and reddened his pipe.

"Do you see that seal down in the cove? Is he not big?" asked I, pointing with my hand.

"Arrah, he is only a baby compared with the giants we used to kill in the Sciarda Rocks long ago."

"And what did you do with them?"

"We sold the pelts and melted the blubber into oil. The female is a wicked animal, especially when she has a young family. One time long ago a fisherman from our village was groping in a dark cave on the Sciarda Rocks. He hit a baby seal with his stick. Then the wonder of the world came over him when the mother seal muttered in Gaelic: 'You had best leave my dear son alone.' That young man never found the taste of health again until the day he died."

"How strange that was," I said.

"The old people claim that seals are under enchantment and have souls just like us. Mind you, but a seal was nearly the cause of my death once."

"Did she bite you?"

"She would if she got the chance. I'll tell you all about it. One early morning, my father told me to take the ass and find out if there was any red weed washed ashore after the night. I straddled the donkey and, on reaching the south shore, was surprised to see a large seal lying on a pile of glossy weed. I left the ass there, took the pitchfork and went between the seal and the mouth of the sea. She growled fiercely at me. I picked up a few stones and hit her again and again. Then I gave her a finishing blow with the handle of the pitchfork. Was I happy when she lay stretched there without a stir! I'll get over three pounds for the skin, not to mention the oil," said I to myself.

"To be sure you had made a good day's pay," I agreed.

"Indeed. I hurried over to the donkey to carry my prize home. But when he saw the dark sleek stranger, the seven battalions of the Fianna could not take a stir out of him. His hide quivered and a dirty wild look came into his eyes. After some coaxing, I blindfolded him with my red muffler and dragged him over to where the seal lay and lifted her up across the baskets that were straddled on for a load of weed. All at once the devil raised his hind legs, struck me in the stomach, let out a wild bray and ran away."

"You were lucky that he didn't kill you," I interrupted, putting a layer of weed on the kiln.

"There I lay in agony and none near to help me. Ah, but what took the wind out of my sails entirely was when I noticed the seal moving. She put her nose in the air and started to slide on her stomach down the cheek of a rock into the water and swam away. To be sure it was only a sleep I put on her. When the donkey reached home and the blindfold on, my people knew that something had gone wrong. Faith, but it was myself that was carried home on the donkey's back like a sack of oats. I had to stay on the rod of my back in bed for a whole week."

"You must have the four-leaved shamrock on you," said I, going out to the stack for some weed.

"Afterward, the ass used to give me a sidelong glance, for he knew what he had done on me. Well, it is growing late, and I'll be easing the kiln down for the mixing and raking," said Red James.

This was a good year for kelp-making, and the shore dwellers were well-pleased with their earnings, though the demands from the stores, landlords and English taxes were also high. One evening in the month of August, the Island boats came back from the kelp market in Kilkerrin. Each boat owner had in his pocket the price of seven or eight tons of kelp at five pounds a ton. To be sure, the woman of the house was in good humor when her man dropped the notes in her lap. It was a night to remember. The villagers went visiting to celebrate with poteen, song and dance, but the men had to wash the black kelp dust out of their skins before their wives would allow them into their beds.

Red James had the price of eight tons. He took out the big tub to the back of the house, stripped off his kelp-soaked clothes, took the roll of bank notes from his pocket and hid it under a stone. He feared that his woman might get her hands on it and allow it to go through her fingers like water through a sieve. Two of his younger sons were busy drawing water from a pot that hung over the fire and spilling it into a tub, while their father scrubbed the coal-like stuff out of his skin. At last the boys poured two buckets of cold water over his head. He stretched his neck and shook his head so that a shower sprayed from his long red beard. He stepped out of the tub clean and happy.

Red James decided to put aside two five-pound notes for a rainy day. He stepped on a chair, glanced warily around to see if anyone was watching, and pushed the two folded bills behind a rafter under a small wooden cross of Saint Brighid. He stepped down, tilted his head back and peered up at the rafter, whispering, "It's just a few inches under the little green cross."

Time passed. The cold dreary winter gave place to a soft spring. Wrack galore was driven ashore by the wind from the west. The Rover had found a pitch pine log in the Oar Inlet that morning. For some time past, Red James was nursing a plan in the back of his mind to have a new pucan built. So he took a stroll along by the shore this evening to see the log the Rover had found.

"By the Book but it is a fine stick," he said to himself, while measuring it with his boot. "Thirty feet long, eighteen inches square, and the grain as straight as an arrow." James did not waste much time until he saluted into the Rover's, whom he found in good humor. He was singing:

> *I'm a jolly sailor and I've sailed the ocean round;*
> *My course I've steered from Mexico*
> *And saved but fifty pound.*
> *I met a maid in——*

"God bless all here," interrupted Red James.

"God and Mary bless yourself, a chara. Move down to the fire and sit on the chair," indicating with his hand. "Is it not the rough kind of weather we are having?"

"That's natural for March. I took a walk by the shore just now and saw that fine log you found. Would you sell it?"

"Since I don't need it myself, that's what I'll do," replied the Rover, rubbing the stubble on his chin.

"I'm going to have a new pucan built."

"I wish you the best of luck, a chara."

"How much would you want for the stick?"

"Three pounds. And only it is yourself that's in it, my soul from the devil, but nobody else would have it for that."

"I'll give you two pounds and not a penny more," Red James replied, standing up as if ready to leave.

"Give me your hand, a chara," smiled the Rover. "I'll make one word with you, son of a generous father. I'll split the difference. Half a sovereign wouldn't last long for either of us in the shebeen."

"I will not break your word," declared James, giving a gentle squeeze to the Rover's hand. "The two pound ten is not at me now, but I'll be back tonight with them. Here is a florin now for earnest."

"As it is the custom I'll take it, but the word of your mother's son is as good as gold," said the Rover, rubbing his palms together.

On reaching his home, Red James thought to himself: "The day of the wind is not the day for the thatching." He stepped nimbly on a chair and put up his hand behind the rafter. His heart began to pound like a triphammer and his mouth went dry as he felt nothing under his fingers. This is the exact spot, too, under the green little cross. Could it move a wee bit? He shoved his hand up and down carefully until the spiders were frightened and ran for their lives. Their nets were never disturbed like this before. Where—where did it go at all, pointing to the yellow rafter as if that stump of bog-oak would answer. He scratched his head and stroked his beard, glancing from the sooty rafter to the maze of broken webs dangling from it.

At long last James had to sit down from the weakness, a coat of sweat covering his face. Now his woman walked boldly in, swaying her hips and humming a lullaby. "Arrah, what is the matter with you, Jimmy, mo mhíle stór," * she smiled, laying her hand on his shoulder.

"Smile away, einseach," † he shouted furiously, shaking his head and glaring at her.

"Musha, what happened to you at all. Are you sick? Your face is an ugly mug covered with dirt. Did you come down through the chimney? Just look at yourself in the mirror!"

"Did you see the two five-pound notes? Did you now? I put them behind that rafter," pointing with a shaking finger and peering at her in suspicion.

"By the Holy Book but I did not, whether it is joking or in earnest you are. You never told me about the money. What a man for a woman to have," she retorted.

"I bought a fine log of pitch pine from the Rover for the new boat we had planned to build. Now, Ann, where is the money gone?"

"By the strength of all the Blessed Books in Rome, but I didn't touch it. How would I know that the money was behind that rafter at all? Maybe the fairies coveted it, God between us and all harm."

Hot with the shame and with a heavy heart, Red James trudged down to the Rover's. He saluted in. The man of

* *mo mhíle stór:* my thousand treasures
† *einseach:* woman fool

the house found a chair for him, and he sat down. "I came to you now, a chara, with bad news. I had two fives hidden at the foot of the rafter and the money is gone."

"I am sorry that you lost the notes, Jim, but as far as I am concerned, it is not a wall to the sky. You can have the wood for the skin of your pucan. The word of your father's son is good enough for me."

'Twas on a Saturday and the sun shone bright to dry the open pit of potatoes in James's haggard. The fine weather was here, and they needs must have a share in the house to cut the slits for the sowing. The older boys carried the spuds in baskets to the house, while the younger lads were running around wild, pelting one another with the old ferns that had covered the pit under the clay.

Chubby little Jimmy toddled over to his father. "Look, look," he said, holding a few scraps of paper in his hand. Red's eyes popped out with wonder as he took the bits from the child. "My soul from the devil," he shouted. His woman, who was stooped down filling the basket, rose to her standing at once and turned around in alarm.

"Where did you find it, son?" he asked, laying his hand on Jimmy's shoulder. The latter, pointing his hand, started to run over with his father along.

"A rat's nest! Ah, but there it is," he exclaimed, picking the bits of paper from the hay, hair and feathers that had made up the nest. "Look now where our hard-earned money went!"

"Mo lein! But you thought otherwise, did you not!" accused his wife. "The hemp rope that was around Joyce's neck broke when the English were in the act of hanging him on the gallows long ago. God had shown the whole world that he was an innocent man."

James gave her a deaf ear and continued to pick out the bits of paper. "How can they ever be joined together?" he moaned, studying a few on the palm of his hand.

"I know not," she replied casually. "But I do know that there are bad, suspicious men in this world."

The following night half a dozen men were sitting around a table in James's house as if they were playing cards. "I have it," one would whisper, handing a scrap of paper to Luke son-of-Paudeen, leader of the gang. One of the five-pound notes being crisp and new was torn into bigger pieces, and the other one being softer was in tiny bits. At long last one five was joined so that the numbers could be read.

"Half a loaf is better than none," smiled Red the next morning when I handed him five singles for the patched bill in our shop.

"Are you not ashamed of yourself now?" said his woman, frowning when he reached home.

"Not a vein in my heart thought for a moment that you had anything at all to do with the money, Ann, a mhíle stór," moving over quietly and giving her a big kiss.

*

Micky O'Shaughnessy, our own tailor, was an honest man and went around from house to house working his trade. He owned a few acres of land where he planted potatoes and some barley in the Spring. His house lay sunk in the sand of the dune, a relic of the distant past when galore huts were built like this. To be sure, they were warm and snug in the winter, and could stand the heavy gales from the west much better than houses built aboveground. Micky also had a small rowboat so that he could go fishing or make a strand of seaweed for manure.

This day the tailor was up with the lark to go raising turf out on the bog at Hare's Ear. With an oar in each hand, he rowed across to Rusheen and ran the boat up on a golden little strand and tied her. He took the sickle, cut a load of ferns, filled the loadrope, tightened it, but then found some trouble trying to rise up under the heavy load. He needs must sit down first with his back to the load, then go on his knees and rise to his standing from there. After leaving the ferns in the boat, he went to the bog and worked hard all day, making little ricks of the dried turf.

A heavy fog fell toward evening. But when the tailor came back for his boat in Rusheen, she was not there. "Ah, some of the Feenish Island lads who were out on the mainland took her," he wailed, starting to shorten the long way home by the road.

The next morning Micky walked the road around by the bridge for his boat, thinking that whoever took her the day before would take her back. But she was still not there. When the tide ebbed, he noticed a bit of rope and the bight around a stone. Pacing back and forth, he saw Grouch coming down the slope. Grouch was a middle-aged man with a black beard and a mean look in his small bleary eyes. He owned thousands of acres of land —land from which the poor tenants had been evicted in years gone by. Nor was he satisfied with all that, but desired to make a bridge of himself and put his hairy arms around the world.

As Grouch approached Micky, he asked in an excited tone, "Did you see a black bull and a speckled calf anywhere around?"

"My little boat is also gone. She was right there yesterday morning," he replied, nodding at the cove.

"Very strange," muttered the other, walking down to the creek along with the tailor.

"See this," said Micky, holding up the frayed bit of warp. "It looks as if some animal had chewed on it. "Would there be any connection between the boat and the bull and the calf?"

"Would the bull chew the rope, step aboard and be gone with the tide?" Grouch added, rummaging in his beard.

"You will drink sooner than myself—I had just thought of the same. The bull and calf might have boarded her to lie on the ferns."

"Ferns!" shouted Grouch. "Stealing them from me, you thief."

"Go on with you. Ferns galore are all over the parish besides yours," the tailor replied, putting his hands on his hips.

"Someone is going to pay me the price of a bull and a calf," Grouch roared back, shaking his finger in the tailor's face.

"Was it me who asked your lazy animals to take my

boat? I don't believe that it was a rabbit who cut the rope? Was it now?"

"The ferns were the cause of it," shouted Grouch, glaring at the tailor and rolling up his sleeves.

The other kept his mouth shut and walked away with his hands behind his back, thinking what a rotten temper the landowner had.

Red James, out with lobster pots on that foggy evening and having to go ashore on Duck Island, was waiting for the mist to lift when he saw a boat drifting down near the Point. He could not see it too clearly due to the fog, but he thought it was a lobster boat and forgot all about it.

"I hope you'll tell me the truth, a chara. Did you see a boat on that misty evening?" asked the tailor.

"As sure as I'm talking to you now. My son, Sean here, saw her also," replied James.

"I thought she was a strange boat when I could see nobody in her but a dark bulk like lobster pots in the hold."

"Ah, a chara, she wasn't strange at all but was mine," cried Micky. "Ochone, never, never will I lay eyes on my dear little boat again. She is gone with the tide far away."

"If I were you," counseled James, "I would pay a visit to the herb-hag. She may give you some advice about the matter."

Micky went to the herb-hag and crossed her palm with a florin. He told her the story of his lost boat and asked her advice on going to law. Her counsel was: "Your boat is gone and forget about her. When you are neither a judge, lawyer, nor peeler, stay out of the court. Not to be known to the law is best for all."

In a short time Micky received a summons from Grouch asking for the price of a bull and calf. Micky did not let his oars go with the current, but gave back the same measure: a summons for the value of the boat. To be sure, the lawyers treated both like two fat geese from the farm. One began to pluck the bull man and the other the boat man. But at long last the day came when the judge of the Ass-sizes in the City of Galway served up his decision.

"Well," he exclaimed, looking down on Grouch. "You have no proof whatsoever that Micky's boat took your bull and calf." Then looking Micky right in the face, "Neither have you any proof that the bull and calf took your boat out to sea. But I do believe myself that the accident couldn't be helped. Therefore, ladies and gentlemen of this court, I dismiss both cases on the merits, so help me God."

The spectators rose to their standing and cheered the verdict.

Poor Micky. He also had the ill luck to marry a woman who was red-headed and much younger than he and whose temper left much to be desired. Indeed, his day of peace vanished when she walked into his home. He loved her dearly and at first tried in one way or another to pacify this temperamental wife.

It was an old custom in the west of Eire, and still is for that matter, to bring home a live fish from the sea on Saint Brighid's Day, which falls on the first day of February. This act is supposed to spark the rest of the year with good luck for the fishermen. It was just noon on this bitter cold day and the tailor hurried to the shore at low ebb. After searching around for some time, peering in slits and crannies, he found a lobster under a weed-coated rock, and with a deal of trouble he caught him. Happily he hurried home with his find.

"Look, a stór," he smiled, standing in the doorway with the fresh lobster in his hand. "I found him down at low-water mark hiding under a boulder. I am wet to the skin as I had to lie on my stomach in a pool of water. The tide had started to flow and I needs must grab him in a hurry. He is a fine big lobster, a stór, and———"

"Come on with you for that is not a lobster," she interrupted, "but a crawfish."

"What are you saying, woman? Sure that is a lobster."

"Lobster my eye! A crawfish is easily known. Can you not see the brown hairs under her belly and the reddish little spikes on her head?"

"A long spike on you! Did you ever see a bald lobster?" turning the crustacean over on the table.

"My own people caught all kinds of fish and shellfish too. Did you not know that? But that is a crawfish—a live crawfish."

"You are wrong, a stór, for that is a lobster."

"You are just trying to make fun of me. She is a crawfish. Ask anyone around."

"You are stubborn. Everyone knows that is a lobster."

"You are a liar and you know it. She is a crawfish—a crawfish," she shrieked, shaking her fist in the tailor's face.

The poor man could not stand it any longer and took the lobster off the table, made for the shebeen and bartered him for poteen. Indeed, Micky was to be pitied trying to please his wife who made hell on earth for him.

"Rise up, a stór, and prepare a mouthful," he said to her a week before Christmas.

"Sleep and food, that is all you desire," she shouted, turning on her back in the bed and stretching her legs. "Are you a man at all? You are going to clean the chimney for so long. The dirty black soot is falling down now in basketfuls and the Holy Season is right on top of us."

"I'm so busy that I haven't the time. But I'll tie the

heatherbroom to a long pole, go up on the roof and push it down through the hole and——"

"A long up on you," she interrupted. "You are going up for so long, but it's little the good you are up or down," slipping out of bed.

Micky got up too, saying while looking for his clothes, "I am going to cut a few blackthorn bushes if you can have some little patience."

"My patience is worn out with you, for you have no vigor or——"

He hurried out the door with a sickle and a loadrope on his shoulder, continuing until he reached a blackthorn bush near the sea. He strolled around looking at the twisted branches. The morning was cold and dreary. A few thrushes were hopping here and there, moaning with the cold and hunger. At last, he returned home with a few crooked branches of blackthorn.

First, he needs must take the fire outside and kindle it at the big boulder. He tied a few branches of the blackthorn in the center of the loadrope and walked up on the roof, letting the end of the rope down to his woman. Then the couple began to pull and tug from each other—up and down, up and down, while the black soot fell in the bed of the fire.

Now Micky closed one eye and peered down the hole with the other. Satisfied, he came down, and went inside saying, "I do think we have made a good job."

She tilted her red head back and looking up in the throat of the chimney. "Look you up there," pointing her finger.

He leaned back to see where she was pointing. "Ah, that is where the branch could not go owing to the crossbar for the pot hanger."

He found the spade, pushed and prodded until a few dabs of soot fell down.

"You did not go far enough as usual with you."

He stepped on a chair and stretched his neck, but that did not satisfy her.

"Sit on the chair, woman, and I'll stand on the back of it. Then maybe——"

She sat down on the seat, and Micky stood up on the back of the chair. At that moment the gray ass pushed in the half-door and grabbed the soda cake on the table.

"The bad luck of the year go with you," she shouted, hurrying over to drive him out.

"Oh, Mhuirre, Mhuirre, Mary the Virgin, I'm killed dead," was all he could say when the chair overturned. "Oh, my ankle is broken," he cried, lying there in the soot and blood flowing from his brow.

"How could I help it when that devil grabbed the bread? But if you had put the staple on the half-door when you came in. . . . I never thought of you at all when I got up off the chair and——"

"You never think right anyway," he moaned as he dragged himself out of the firebed and tried to stand up.

"I'll run over to the weaver right now and get some sprain thread from him to heal your ankle," she said, heaping a mountain of cobwebs on his brow to stop the bleeding.

This tailor, Micky, was a short hardy little man with a sallow skin. His dark hair was thick and the curls in the back and sides were reaching up for the brim of his caubeen. He always had a stubble of dark beard, heavy eyebrows and his lips had a comical twist. At times a worried look shadowed his blue eyes as if some evil was knocking at his conscience. He was a good tailor, the best in the parish. What parish? The whole county I mean. Yet, his own suit was often shabby and looked as if it were thrown on him with a pitchfork.

But he was a changed man when he visited our house one morning to make a suit for my father. His crios* was neatly tied around the waist of his gray homespun trousers, his vest buttoned and the red muffler around his neck tucked neatly inside. Over his vest he wore a clean white woolen bawneen with the corners tucked under the multi-colored crios. A new caubeen of dark flannel sat at a rakish angle on his head. A strong pair of boots made by the village bootmaker shone from a fresh coat of dogfish liver oil. Faith, but Micky was a new man as he fondled the bale of frieze that lay on our table.

"Musha, Jimeen of my heart, when will I be making a man out of you, or will you keep on that gray petticoat until you'll find a woman?" he smiled and peeled off his bawneen and muffler. I had fine cipeens† touching the fire, and I watching to have them at the right burn for to mark the flannel. But Micky made me so angry that I pitched the markers into the fire with the tongs. A longing for trousers was on me, but there was still a tuck in the petticoat that my growth must match when let out before I could have the pants.

With some trouble the tailor pulled a line out of his pocket and a piece of chalk. He measured Daida up and down and around the waist. That was all—the other dimensions were in his head.

"Let the house be at the tailor now," laughed my father

* *crios:* woven belt
† *cipeens:* small chips or sticks of wood

as he walked out the doorway to go gathering seaweed on the strand.

"Mo lein!" sighed Micky. "Many is the home that forgets the tailor. To be sure, some people suspect that he is in clover, flowers and honey along with the women. Forgotten entirely I had been while making a suit of clothes in the west of the Island some time ago. A bulog for the dinner was baking on the hearth. The woman of the house took the lid off the oven and shouted, 'May the devil take you—you are a long time there and not baked yet,' taking the red off the lid so that the poor tailor would have his dinner and supper in one. When I found her gone outside, I stepped down from the table and heaped a mountain of red on the lid. The smell from the burning bread hurried her in, mind you."

Not a word did he say for a while, his head tilted to one side, the tip of his tongue sticking out from the corner of his mouth and his lips imitating the scissors as they opened and closed cutting the flannel. When that trouser leg was cut, he took the curve out of his back and continued. " 'Who put the fire on the oven?' she asked, glaring at me and hitting the red with the tongs to ease her anger.

" 'I thought you wished me to do it,' replied I.

" 'God barely set the soul in some men,' she snapped as she set the bulog in front of me with a bang. The cake was badly burned. I dug out the inside and pitched the rest to the dog who did not complain."

"Is she a scrawny red-haired woman?" asked my mother, putting a wise look on her face.

The tailor didn't let on he heard, but continued. "The next day my meals were in regular order, for she had bought sense."

As he started to fold up the various pieces of cloth, he asked with a laugh, "Musha, did you ever hear about Macheen the fool? He wanted a new suit, so some trickster told him to find a lively shore crab, spread the end of a bale of frieze on the table, take a scissors and cut as the crab walked. When Macheen had found his people gone to church, he brought a crab from the shore, smoothed the gray flannel on the white pine table and told the crab that he wanted a suit for himself. The crab was silent and started to walk. Macheen took hold of the scissors and followed the crab's backside until a good share of the bale was cut."

"He must be feeble-minded," my mother said.

"Not a spark of sense was in his head, no more than the day he was born," replied the tailor, wiping the table of imaginary dust with his sleeve. Then he took off his boots and laid them on the windowsill out of the dog's reach.

"Watch likes the cod-liver oil," he laughed as he stepped nimbly on the table, made the sign of the Cross on his forehead and sat down cross-legged and began to sew. Great wonder was on me seeing him thread the needle while looking the other way, talking all the time to someone. He yawned and made the sign of the Cross in his open mouth with his right thumb.

"Why did you do that?" I asked, looking up at him.

"Did you ever hear what happened to Noble Peter long ago?" he asked and changed the crossing of his legs. "Myself saw it happen, for I was at the Cashel fair the very same day with a pig. Noble Peter had a fatter one and maybe the poor man didn't sleep much the night before, but watching for the midnight strand to drive the animal out to the mainland. Indeed, there was a sharp demand for pigs because there were many other jobbers there besides the Galway rogues."

"The Galway buyers always gang up against the strangers," added my mother as she made the table ready for the meal.

"True for you. But this day the rival buyers were racing each other at the dawn of day and buying pigs a mile outside the town. In the evening as usual we all gathered in a pub to wet our lips. All of a sudden we were startled by a strange howl. On turning around we saw Noble Peter and his mouth so wide open that a goose could have flown into it."

Mama interrupted, "Come over now, Micky, and have a mouthful. You too, son."

Was I happy to sit down at the same table with the tradesman! Though I was hungry, yet I leaned back in the chair to bask in the glory.

"Don't be bashful on account of me, Jimeen," said the tailor, pushing the plate of pancakes toward me. Then he filled a glass of poteen from a brown cruiskeen, raised the glass and toasted: "Here is good health, my good generous woman, and slainte Jimeen, too." Nodding at me, "May your wife be a fine colleen, may your house be built on a hillock and not like mine down in the ground."

He put the full of my skin of anger on me and I started eating the pancakes. Why had he always the bad manners to talk about women? I asked myself. On finishing the meal, he took out his pipe and put a leg over the other. Had he forgotten the story and left poor Peter there with his mouth wide open?

"Then what happened to Noble Peter?" I eagerly asked and turned out from the board.

"Where was I?" knitting his eyebrows.

"Where Peter's mouth was so wide open that a goose could fly into it."

"Right," he smiled, patting me on the head. "Sean Pheggy, Darach Mor and the rest of the company put down their glasses and tried to comfort him as he was in pain. A man hurried for the priest and another for the doctor."

" 'The lock of his jaw is a kind of jammed. Hold him down and we'll try to unlock it,' " whispered Darach Mor, and he began to rub the jaw.

Then he did like this: "Open your mouth, Jimeen," the tailor ordered me, laying the palm of one hand on the top of my head and snapping a blow with the other under my chin. "That was all that was to it," he laughed. "Before the priest or doctor had arrived on the scene, not only was Noble Peter's jaw unlocked but his heart as well. He slapped down on the counter a five-pound note and ordered drinks for all hands."

※

There was a man on our Island, Tom, son of John Greene, nicknamed the Jobber because he was a dealer in cattle. He was well on in years and not married yet. Perhaps he never had the time for he was so busy going from fair to fair. He had a nice holding of land and was a clever buyer and seller. Therefore, many is the colleen that had her eye on him.

This day Tom sailed in his boat across the bay on some business. He met up with Mrs. Connolly at the pier. She was picking periwinkles to sell in her little shop. Tom was a handsome middle-aged man and not shy or backward either. So he began to joke with the plump dark-haired widow, Seemingly she found no fault in the least with his banter and in the end invited him to her home.

The Jobber was a good churchgoer and a pillar of strength in the parish. One Sunday as he was on his way from the chapel in his jaunting car, a lady, named Mrs. Burke, was walking along the road ahead of him. He stopped the car.

"Will you have a lift along with me, Madam?" he asked politely.

She graciously accepted. Tom drove her home, and she invited him in for a cup of tea. The couple talked about this and that as they ate the tasty lunch Mrs. Burke prepared.

"I'm very lonesome myself since my man left me. He had a kind of wandering lust and couldn't help it. But I have found out that he is dead, may God be good to his soul. You must be lonesome yourself, Tom, living on that Island."

"Well, I must be on my way," and he rose to his standing. "Even on a Sunday there are chores galore to be done. Thank you very much for the tea and it's a great pleasure to know you."

"I hope you'll come again soon," smiled Mrs. Burke, escorting him to the door.

Tom sailed oftener in his pucan across the bay. He would pay a visit to Mrs. Connolly to buy the groceries and have a chat.

"How can you live all alone, Tom?" she asked, as they drank the tea.

"What can I do? It's hard to find a reliable servant."

"Find a woman for yourself, a stór. You'll only live once. I'm so lonely myself since my poor husband drowned a few years ago. May dear God be kind to his soul and——" She turned toward Tom, sobbing. "Why am I telling all this to you?"

The Jobber went oftener to the cobbler even if he had to rip his boots, for charming Mrs. Burke lived next door. This evening after leaving his shoes at the bootmaker, he hurried to see Mrs. Burke, who happened to be a dressmaker. She had the kettle boiling as usual as she saw him coming.

"Céad míle fáilte, hundred thousand welcome. Why don't you come more often?"

"I haven't the time as I have so much to do. I needs must be going now. I have the cows to look after."

"Take it easy, a stór, and watch your health. Find someone to give you a hand and cook your meals. The tea is ready now."

She led him into the parlor and talked as they enjoyed

the meal. "Call me Nora from this out," she said, "and we'll get along much better."

Tom told her all about himself and the jobbing business.

"Would you like to see the new dress that I have just finished?" bringing him into a back room. "I make good money even if I say so myself. What do you think of the dress?"

"It is a beauty, dear Nora, pure silk and well-made," smiled Tom, feeling the texture of the blue garment.

"It is for my ownself, too. Just a minute until I'll try it on."

"You look lovely, dear Nora," said Tom, patting her on the back.

"But I feel so alone," and she began to sob and moan.

Gallant Tom took out his handkerchief and dried her tears, giving her a light kiss on the cheek and whispering in her ear, "Don't cry, a stór."

She gazed into his eyes of blue and began stroking his dark curly hair until he put his arms around her waist and kissed her.

Tom got his boots from the cobbler and went home at the fall of night well-pleased with himself.

Nora had a perfect figure and was a neat dresser and she thought that she would be on the pig's back if she lured him into marriage. A fine honest man, strong and healthy. When his and hers would be put together it would be Heaven on earth. The Connolly woman was thinking about the same.

But then there was Joe Kennedy, Tom's neighbor, who had a fine strapping girl as a daughter. On her way home from church one day after finishing a Novena, the sky darkened and the thunder rumbled in the distance. She hurried along for the nearest shelter, which just happened to be Tom's home. She was just inside the door when the lightning flashed and the thunder crashed. The rain stood like sticks on the flags outside. Tom put a céad míle fáilte before her, made the tea and they were cozy enough in each other's company. Shelia was up in the clouds and thought that God Himself had sent the thundershower in answer to her prayer. She had overed two-score years but was not behindhand at all as a lover.

One early morning Shelia dressed herself in her Sunday best and saluted into the herb-hag's home.

"God bless all here," she whispered, glancing around to find out was the seeress alone.

"God and Mary bless yourself, a stór," replied the hag of the herb. "Sit down on the stool near the fire, for the morning is a kind of sharp."

"I didn't come to sit or stay. It is a good while back since I was here before. Do you remember? I hope you won't fail on me now, as I'm at the end of my rope. I was here before, but that was all the good of it. Pat Kelly, God be with him, married that fat hussy from the hill though I loved him. But I love this new man, Tom, better than anyone I ever knew. He is so gentle and kind to me and kind to everyone. He even visits a poor widow whose husband was lost at sea to comfort her."

"Comfort, how are you! Your grain is ground, a stór. A widow will never give up the struggle for a man. Her grip is much the same as the limpet on the rock. Whilst she might pretend to be lonely weeping for the departed, she is eagerly watching her chance and ready to pounce on her victim like a hungry hawk on a sparrow."

"To the Devil with her," snapped Shelia.

"And to the seven devils," added the seeress. "But they

have the knack and knowledge, and a single man is like a baby in a widow's claw. Just the same I'll do my best for you," handing her the herbs and liquor.

"Thank you," smiled Shelia warmly. "If all goes well, I'll give you a gold sovereign for good measure," walking out the door with a light step. On her way home she was thinking hard: How could she manage at all to put the herbs in his clothing unknown to him.

Night fell and the full moon rolled up in the clear sky, which was flecked with stars. I won't sleep a wink tonight, God help me, Shelia said to herself as she sat knitting by the fireside. All at once, an idea came to her: the new muffler—could she not sew along the edges bits of the herb the hag had given her.

Tom came the next evening. She made the tea and put in a little of the magic liquid the hag had given her. After he had finished the tasty meal, Shelia said warmly, "I have a new muffler made for you and I wonder will you like it?" bringing it down from the room. "Try it on now, Tom."

"It is beautiful with all the colors of the rainbow. How can I ever repay you for your kindness, a stór?" putting his arms around her waist and kissing her.

"The charm is working already," thought she to herself.

Tom strolled home that night as light as a starling. Shelia was happy, too, facing the mirror and fixing her long reddish hair before going to bed. Next evening Tom visited her again wearing the rainbow muffler, and the lovers had an enjoyable time. Wasn't it in Kennedy's that most of his turf was cut and dried now, and old Joe himself had much respect for Tom.

"Keep the muffler on in this cold weather, a stór," she whispered as he kissed her at the door.

Shelia sang to herself as she worked around the house. Indeed, he was as good as hers already. This evening she went to the well for a can of fresh water and met her friend, Siobhan Fhada.

"Siobhan," Shelia whispered, a bit excited. "I have a big secret to tell but never let it beside your breath, will you?"

"Not at all. You know me, a stór."

"Tom Greene and myself are going to be married. He hasn't asked me yet, but I know he will."

"He is a fine honest man, well-off too. I wish you both all the luck in the world."

Siobhan could not shelter the secret long. On leaving the water inside, she hurried over to Maire Sally to borrow a pinch of salt. "I just boiled an egg and found out that I had no salt."

"I'll put a few grains in this cup and you may bring it back again."

"Did you hear any news lately?" asked Siobhan in a whisper.

"News, a stór?"

"You didn't hear about Shelia Kennedy?" said Siobhan, sitting on the stool beside Maire. "She is going to marry Tom Greene, the Jobber. Never tell anyone. Shelia herself told me and warned me to keep it a secret," pressing her hand on the other's knee.

No sooner had Siobhan left than Maire rushed out to the next-door neighbor and told the secret to the woman of the house. So the news flew fast from mouth to mouth until at length Mrs. Connolly heard it. She had not seen Tom for some time and was growing uneasy.

"I knew it, I knew it all along," she cried. "He never

came next or near me for a fortnight. Coming in here and I so kind to him making tea and sweet cakes for the scoundrel and he lying to me all the time. Arrah, who would ever think that he'd do such a foul deed to a broken-hearted widow?"

Mrs. Burke on learning about it fainted. When she revived, she moaned, "I cannot believe it. Tom was so kind, gentle and honest—a perfect gentleman, and then——" She couldn't say a word more, threw herself on the bed which creaked in sympathy as the heart-broken Nora sobbed and tossed from side to side.

The widows were furious. What hurt most was the blow to their pride. Now they were the laughing stock of the parish: Would they let the blackguard have his way? Certainly not! So the two joined forces in a common cause and had Tom summoned to stand before the bar of justice for breach of promise.

"We only want fair play," they told anyone who wished to listen. "And we are going to get it from the British Law. Her Majesty, Queen Victoria, is herself a lonely widow."

In due time, Tom was handed a summons by the process-server. His mouth went dry and a lump came in his throat, for he knew well that he was in the claw of the hammer. One female would be bad enough, but two as a team was hell let loose. Should he then sell out all his property and escape to some foreign land? He hurried over to Sean Pheggy for advice.

"God bless all here," he saluted in.

"God and Mary bless yourself, Tom. Draw down to the hearth, for it's a trifle sharp."

"How is the world treating you, Sean? You have on your mind to go after the fish?" He was mending a trammel net.

"No use complaining, a chara. How is everything with yourself?"

"I'm in real trouble, a stór. I do need your counsel right now."

"What could the matter be, Tom?"

"The likes of it has never happened before in the parish or in the country, either. To be caught in the meshes of the law is bad enough, but I'll be cursed by the clergy, too. Women, a chara, and widows at that. I am——"

"A widow has you sued, I bet," interrupted Sean, laying down the net pin and tugging at the tuft of goat's whisker on his chin.

"A pair of them for breach of promise."

Sean burst out laughing and slapped his thigh, "What do you think about that?"

Tom frowned and snapped back. "It's no laughing matter!"

Sean straightened his face, saying, "I'm very sorry, Tom. Have they any genuine case against you: witnesses, letters or anything like that? You know what I mean?"

"You know the Connolly widow who has the little shop across the bay? I used to deal there for groceries and have a chat with her now and again. And I also used to visit Mrs. Burke, the dressmaker, and had tea along with her a few times. I never wrote or promised to marry either one of them."

"I'm surprised at you, Tom. But what on earth did you want in the dressmaker's anyway?" chuckled Sean.

"I used to go to the bootmaker's next door and while he'd be doing the mending, I'd stroll into Mrs. Burke's to pass the time. I think you know her. She is the one who had left her husband by himself some time ago."

"Who doesn't know that rip? Ah, you rascal. You are

in a mess all right. I should know as I was spliced to a widow once. No firmer will the limpet clutch to the rock than the widow will clutch on to her man. Should he kill her, he'd be hung in a decent manner, but if he don't he'll be in misery for the rest of his life."

"This is no joke, Sean," replied Tom. "They are planning to ruin me. And I'd better settle with them right away."

"Are you clean out of your mind! Settle with them? Then you'd have made your own coffin and crawled into it, and all they'd have to do is to nail down the lid."

"I am just thinking of selling out and sailing across the ocean to Canada. What would you say to that?"

"No, no! You wouldn't go very far. Never give up or run away, Tom, but fight it out to the bitter end. The man with courage never lost."

"Thank you so much, Sean. I'll follow your advice come what may."

"That's the right spirit, Tom. Good luck to you, my friend."

This morning was clear and the sun pouring down her pleasant warmth. The low-lying meadows near the shore steamed in a hazy shimmer. There was not a sound save the faint melody of a lark lost high in the blue heavens. Poor Tom was praying diligently, leaning on the garden wall and glancing down the bohreen now and again.

Luke, who was helping him, came out of the barn with a sickle in his hand and said, "Let's be going now."

Tom blessed himself, put the beads in his pocket, found his reaping hook and paused to think. "But maybe it isn't worth my while to start. You know that this is the day." And he looked gloomily at the road.

"I'm tired telling you not to pay any heed to the court," Luke growled.

"Surely the peelers will drag me there by force," moaned Tom, throwing his sickle on the ground and spitting at it.

"Let them try to take you. What do you think I'd be doing?"

Tom did not reply, but was watching the heavy ears of rye waving in the light wind. In a short time the reapers heard the dogs barking.

"Ah, they are coming. I'll go along with them of my own will. You can cut the rye and take it easy."

"Have it your own way, but you are a big fool."

Just then two peelers came to the wall. "We have a warrant for your arrest, Tom Greene. Your presence is urgently needed right now down yonder at the court house. Come along with us, will you?"

"What for?" queried Tom, with innocence upon him.

"You should know. Something bad you have done on the women."

"What women, may I ask?"

"Imposter. Come along and waste no more time."

Tom, afraid of the court, put on his coat and muffler and followed the limbs of the law. Shelia, who happened to be on her way home from church, met them. On seeing Tom along with the saucer caps, her mouth went dry.

"Where are you going?" she asked, a quiver in her voice.

"To the courthouse."

"Get a move on there," shouted one of the peelers, pushing Tom ahead as he stood in the middle of the road talking to Sheila.

"What's it about, a stór?" she whispered, walking along beside him.

"They told me it was something about women."

Shelia was silent. A lump came into her throat. As they marched along the highway, women were standing in the doorways and peeking out through windows hoping to find a glimpse of poor Tom. They were full of sympathy for him. But the men working in the fields rested on their spade handles thinking that a spell in prison was too good for him.

Nearing the courthouse, they were met by a band of ruffians who were shouting: "The widows are waiting ready to tear you apart, Tom, and make food for the sparrows out of your carcass. Die like a true-born Gael and the poets will praise you in song."

The courtroom was packed as Tom walked in. The plaintiffs began to scream: "Look at the blackguard who deceived one of us and then the other. But now we want nothing more to do with him, only to see justice performed."

As the cases were called in alphabetical order, the widows headed the list. "Mrs. Burke and Mrs. Connolly against Tom Greene, for breach of promise," called the judge.

The women walked up to the rails holding their heads high.

"Swear on this," ordered the clerk of the court, "and repeat after me: I do solemnly swear that I'll tell the truth and nothing but the truth so help me God."

Each woman kissed the black Book.

"Did Tom Greene promise to marry you?" asked the judge of Mrs. Burke. "And you also?" turning to Mrs. Connolly.

"He did indeed, your worship, and stayed at our homes morning, noon and night," the two ladies replied as one.

"Tom Greene, come up here," called the judge.

Tom walked to the rail with a heavy step, swore on the black Book and kissed it.

"What is your name?" asked the judge.

"My nickname you mean, your Lordship?"

There was much laughter in the court.

The judge pounded his gavel. "Your name, you woodenhead."

"Didn't you call me by my name before, your Honor?"

"Your right name," shouted the judge angrily.

"Tom Greene, your Worship."

"You are accused by Mrs. Burke and Mrs. Connolly of breach of promise."

"These women are telling a pack of lies, your Honor. I never promised to marry either one of them. I used to buy a few groceries in Mrs. Connolly's shop, and the other one invited me in to have a cup of tea and to show me the dresses she was making."

Mrs. Burke kept shaking her head at the defendant and began to sob. The Connolly lady began to claw the air, roaring like a breaker nearing the shore. The judge rapped for order, but the breaker still thundered on until, with strength spent, ran down on its own accord foaming at the mouth.

"Tom Greene," spoke the judge in a grave tone, "are you trying to make a bridge of yourself over Her Majesty's law and deceive the ladies, asking them to marry you and then deserting them in their hour of need? What could be the matter with you at all?"

"As God is my Judge, I never had anything at all to do with them, your Honor, but they must be schemers."

"I have just heard that you are entangled with another female, too. Are you a real pagan?"

"Who told you that, your Highness?"

"Mrs. Connolly over there knows all about it," indicating with his hand.

"Indeed, I do, your Honor, and that is the other one," pointing a shaking finger toward Shelia.

"Is that true, Tom Greene?" asked his Lordship.

"She is a neighbor and a good friend of mine, your Honor, and I visit her home now and again."

Poor Shelia grew red in the face, glanced down at the floor, but never opened her mouth.

"Musha, look at that hussy blushing," shouted Mrs. Connolly, "who has no more shame in her than an alley cat."

"Shut your mouth, woman," shouted the Judge, pounding his gavel.

"Tom Greene," said his Lordship in a solemn tone, "what is the matter, or is the devil kindling under you? Involved with three women at the same time! I needs must say that you have courage."

"Those connivers need a man in the worst way, your Honor, and they think that I'm an easy mark," said Tom in a polite tone.

The widows started to scream. The judge pounded his gavel. The clerk threatened to put them out, and they ran down on their own like an old alarm clock.

"Have the plaintiffs any witnesses or letters to bolster their claim against Greene, the defendant?" asked the Judge.

"What witnesses or letters do we need, your Highness? To be sure the whole county knows all about this man's foulness to women."

"But this is a court of law and the defendant denies everything," said the Judge.

"Then there is no justice at all in this world," shouted the widows. "We'll appeal the case to the Big Assizes next

March. The Queen herself is a lonely widow and she'll understand."

"Tom Greene, the defendant," called his Lordship. "You must marry one of the ladies, and that might keep you out of mischief."

The widows stirred in their seats and beamed all over. Now they felt a kind of mean for being so hard on poor Tom.

"One of the plaintiffs, your Honor?" pointing his hand.

"You blockhead. One of the females you are entangled with. No more dillydallying. Let's finish this up. Make your choice right now, Tom Greene!"

"Then I'll marry the maid, your Honor."

"Case dismissed on the merits. Next case," called the Judge.

Poor Shelia fainted away. A court attendant hurried into the room with a can of fresh water to sprinkle some on the prostrate woman. But Mrs. Connolly snatched the vessel out of his hand and pitched the can and all in the face of Shelia, which revived her at once.

*

The women young and old take much delight in telling and retelling stories about this one and that one who are great with each other. Whether these tales be true or not makes little difference when they themselves believe in them. Especially in Spring, the season for matchmaking.

One morning Maire daughter-of-Sally came running up to my mother as she was cutting seed potatoes. "Musha, did you hear of anyone stirring out?"

"They say that Marc son-of-Mickil was looking for a woman across the bay. Darach Mor and the Changeling were along with him."

"She was a returned Yank," added Little Nan, who was helping Mama to cut the slits.

"Great luck was on him," snapped Old Pheggy, who sat on the hob smoking a dudeen. "Anyone who has spent a term across the sea is not much no-how, and, if they have any taste of money at all, the devil himself is in the hearts of the stingy misers."

"True," agreed Nan, hastily amending, "If that colleen had not any eye somewhere else, she'd long for any Marc."

"It's a wonder that Sean son-of-Nora is not stirring out," said Mama, rising up to hang down the kettle.

"Nor did he lose the tooth with the music in it yet," giggled Old Pheggy, pushing back stray wisps of hair under her headkerchief.

"Ah, but the poor creature is very shy and nervous," sighed Nan, peering closely at the eye of a British Queen to figure out how she could get the most slits.

"I was so nervous myself that memorable evening when I got married that I wished for a bolt of lightning to come and strike me," Maire put in.

"A long bolt on you," chuckled Pheggy, whose face was wrinkled like an old potato. "You didn't know what sky was nearest you that very night with the hot flame of eagerness that swept over you."

Sean son-of-Nora was a fine young man, tall, slender and blond. He lived along with his mother in a thatched cottage near the shore. They had a nice holding of land, a few cows and some sheep. Sean had just finished the Spring sowing and had an idea not to let his oars with the current. So he told his mother that he wished to go looking for a woman.

"Good enough, son," she warmly replied. "Didn't I tell you before that it was about time? Good luck."

One night Darach Mor strolled into Old Paudeen's where a crowd of us was playing cards. "Know ye not, lads, that the night is rather short now for night visiting?"

"Ah, but the poor boys will have to be somewhere," said the woman of the house, putting a few sods of turf on the fire. "I heard that Sean Nora himself is going to stir out at last."

"A springtime story maybe," replied the other casually, reddening his pipe with an ember.

"Not a word of a lie in it," she smiled, pressing her hand on Darach's knee.

"A maid won't hamper his growth anymore," said Darach, shrewdly rising to his standing to go home.

Darach and myself went part of the way home together, and he told me about Sean's wedding plans. "You needs must be ready too next Monday night," he whispered.

On the appointed evening I walked into Sean Nora's house. Darach and Sonny Tom were sitting on chairs near the fire. A few bottles of poteen were standing on the table. Sean filled the glasses and handed them around. In a short time we were on our way to the pier. The moon was moving up in the star-flecked sky, silvering a path on the bay. A dismal roar could be heard from Tramore in the west as the cool waves broke on the silvery sand. Dogs barked and asses brayed in the distance. We hoisted the sails on the pucan, and with the fair wind it did not take us long to reach the mainland. After mooring the boat we took a few swallows from a bottle, for there were a few miles to tramp through heather-clad hills before reaching Gleannnasmol, the Vale of the Thrushes, where the colleen lived. This village was nestled in the lap of a hill and many tall bens around. A small lake lay like a mirror in the valley, and the moon patch on the surface shone like the scales of bass.

The house was in darkness as all had gone to bed. The dog barked at us. Darach knocked on the door, and the man of the house, Peter, got up to let us in.

"You must be cold and hungry, men. Draw down to the hearth," invited Peter, finding chairs for us and kindling a fire.

"We need no food, a chara, but we'll have a drink together," smiled Darach, putting the bottles on the table. The woman of the house and the son and daughter got up and put a céad míle fáilte before us.

Darach divided the poteen and in a short time Peter was pleasantly lit, saying, "Give us a verse of a song, Darach."

Darach cleared his throat and began in the Gaelic:

If I had a small boat I'd sail the wide sea,
Or write a long letter my true love to please.
Mo lein! that I'm not with my own love so true,
Alone all the night in the bright pearly dew.

"May the Lord not weaken you," smiled Peter, taking a cruiskeen out of a press and standing it on the table. Peter was well over six feet tall and as straight as a candle.

"Give me your hand," said Darach to the man of the house. "We came here tonight, a chara, Jimeen, Sonny and myself on a very special mission to ask for the hand of your daughter, Maire, for Sean son-of-Nora, may God bless them both. It is not necessary to praise him. He'd be praised if I never opened my mouth. Measure the parish and weigh it. Parish, I said, but it was the county I meant—and you never would find the likes of him. He has a fine house and a holding of land well-stocked with cows and sheep. He owns a fast sailing boat with the big sea and all her wealth of fish and weed at his doorstep. This fine young man Sean Og Kennedy never drank or smoked and is at peace with the world. Never did see the inside of a courtroom, either. I sum up now, a chara, without fear of contradiction that your daughter could not find his equal anywhere on this earth."

During that speech Sean did not stir but kept looking into the heart of the fire. Mother, father, son and daughter marched into a bedroom to talk it over. In a few minutes they came out saying as with one voice, "It is up to Maire, herself, for it is her own life she has to spend." Maire blushed and smiled, glancing over at Sean, who smiled back.

"Let's have another drink," suggested Darach, filling the glasses. "Here's a toast to Maire and Sean's health and happiness galore, and may they live on and on until they see their children's children and the fourth generation."

Maire was a tall blonde, and her sparkling blue eyes had been set on Sean for many a day.

"May we all live in peace and health," smiled Peter, brushing back his thick blond hair with the palm of his hand.

"I'll call on the priest during the week and have a talk with him about the marriage," said Sean as Maire and himself walked out ahead to have a little chat together.

"Good night to ye and pleasant dreams," said Darach, Sonny and myself as with one voice.

All of us shook hands with the man and woman of the house, also with Maire and the fine handsome son, Tom.

"God's blessing be with ye and a safe trip home," chorused the whole family.

We took the shortcut through the purple heather to the pier. The ring of dawn was brightening the eastern sky when we reached our Island home.

*

The success of Sean son-of-Nora inspired Paudeen son-of-Tom, who was a small lanky fellow and the laziest man in the village. Why could he not pick a wife from the mountain too? Indeed, she would have to be from a distant part, for Paudeen's shiftless ways were well-known even outside the Island. No girl with a spark of sense in her head would glance in the side he would be or consider him for a moment.

One evening Paudeen lay stretched on a hillock thinking deeply of marriage. Festy, the mountaineer, happened to come along and saluted.

"God bless you, Paudeen. Is it not a fine evening?"

"The same blessing to you, a chara. It is glorious weather, praise be to the Lord."

"How are you carrying yourself?"

"Not so good at all, Festy. When I see everyone stirring out and myself left behind like Oisin after the Fianna."

"Arrah, what is the matter with you. Why don't you look for one? You know right well that she won't come into the house to you."

"True, a chara. Do you know of any woman up in the hills?"

"There is a woman, and if it is not her there is another and still another. We'll have a chat about it tonight, for I am in a hurry now down to Mickileen Liam's house to buy some cured fish."

Three nights afterward, Darach Mor and Sonny son-of-Tom went along with Paudeen, carrying a few bottles of poteen in their pockets. It was early on a Monday night when they left the Island, for the road was long to Bailebeagghleannuaigneachnamuicemoireduibhe, the little village of lonely valley of the big black pig, up in the mountains.

It was late in the night when they reached the house of Colm Keane, who had three daughters. They asked for the eldest, Brighid, a dark slender girl with delicately chiseled features. The match was made right away between herself and Paudeen. Indeed, he had well-trained men along who left no stone unturned to gain their objective. Paudeen smiled to himself and laughed inside while they took turns praising him and those who came before him. As the Islanders were leaving for home the man of the house said, rubbing his dark sideburns thoughtfully, "I think I'll take a tour into the Island next week to make a few arrangements about the wedding."

One day Colm came down from the mountain not so much about the wedding arrangements but to find out a little about Paudeen. Colm had on a new suit of gray homespuns. He was careful about his appearance and, as he was drawing near to his future son-in-law's, he washed the dust off his face and combed his dark hair using a pool of water for a mirror. He found Paudeen lying on the hillock at the gable end.

The latter rose to his standing at once and said smilingly, "Céad míle fáilte, Colm, friend of my heart," shaking hands warmly with the mountaineer. "Come on inside until you'll have a mouthful to eat."

They drank a few glasses of poteen and ate a good meal. Paudeen took Colm out then to show him his own little patch of ground, but added on a strip of his neighbor's land. Then he pointed to the shore—the wild rocks and the breakers where his red, brown and black weeds, sea rods and laminaria grew; the big endless sea itself where many millions of fish, lobsters, crawfish, crabs, oysters, scallops, soles, plaice and flounders were waiting to be caught.

"By the Book, but ye are in a kind of Paradise," smiled the mountaineer.

"And more," boasted Paudeen. "The wrack too: bags of flour, pipes of wine, puncheons of rum, barrels of paraffin, petrol, aceltone and bales of cotton. Big logs of mahogany, rosewood, pitch pine and teak are often washed ashore from the ships that were sunk in the Atlantic."

"We have heard all about the wrack in the mountains."

"Faith, but the evening looks as if it would blow," said Paudeen, studying the clouds. "I might as well let more slack with the cables of the hooker. Will you come out to see the boat, a chara?"

A neighbor, Colm, and himself rowed out to the hooker in a punt. After Paudeen coiled some ropes, let some slack with the anchor cable and fustered with the halyards and sail covers, the neighbor asked, "Where is the hooker-man himself?"

"Shush, shush and don't make a social blunder," whispered Paudeen, winking his eye. This stranger is the father of my wife-to-be and I'd like to make a good impression so that he won't be stingy with the dowry."

After looking the boat all over, Colm said, "She is a fine big boat and must be a fast sailer, too, God bless her."

"She is a strong seaworthy hooker, nor are there many in Galway Bay that could pass her out," replied Paudeen offhand, as they stepped on board the punt to row back to shore.

The mountaineer was as light as a starling as he shortened the road home on the next day.

"Musha, how did you like the Island?" his woman asked anxiously, as soon as he walked in. The rest of the family were sitting around the fire eager to hear the news.

"Very good indeed. He has a fine holding of land, miles of shore and breakers full of seaweed, duilisg and carrigeen. The big ocean itself at his very doorstep full of fish and lobsters. He has a splendid hooker that can carry forty tons. What a beauty! There was luck galore in store for our colleen, thank God. She could search the whole wide world and would not find a grander place."

The family were delighted, and his wife's round moon face beamed with pleasure as she listened to his soft voice reciting every detail.

The day of the wedding was fine. The mountaineer had poteen and wine galore the night before to treat the house. Many of the shore-dwellers tramped to the hill to enjoy themselves and help drink the mountain dew. A large crowd had already gathered at the chapel for the ceremony.

The church was packed just as if they were beaten in by the back of an ax. Those who were massed near the door could not keep still for a moment, swaying and scratching the floor with their hobnailed boots. The lights trembled from the two big candles on the altar. Indeed, it was more like a rowdy dance hall than a house of prayer. Those who were merry at the "Time" the night before were tipsy galore now and making a ree-rah in the back. A tall gray-haired priest clad in white vestments stepped out from the Sacristy. When he spoke angrily, the church quieted down. Little Martin Kennedy, a tawny-faced old man, walked ahead of the couple clearing a path right up to the altar.

The Holy Father was waiting inside the rail. In a short time, the bride and groom with the witnesses were lined up. His Reverence began to read out of a Book, but when he raised his head he noticed that the bridal party were not in the regular order for the ceremony. Brighid Colm, the bride, was already half-married to the Changeling, who was one of the witnesses.

"Keep in your proper places," said the priest, pushing the bridegroom back to his place. Poor Paudeen got so nervous that he went wrong again. The four would remind one now of a half-set danced by amateurs as in and out they shuffled. The church roared and the Holy Father grew more angry.

"Where is the ring now?" asked the priest impatiently.

"Father, I put it in this pocket," gasped Paudeen, in a shaky voice and the sweat rolling down his cheeks.

The Changeling gave a hand in the search and found the ring in the bridegroom's vest pocket.

Paudeen's hand shook so much that instead of putting the ring on the bride's finger, it fell and rolled down the floor. Instantly, the Changeling jumped over the rails, planted his foot on it, and the crowd roared. His Reverence put his whole mind on the job now with an eye on the couple and the other on the Book until he had them spliced.

When the marriage was over, those who had horses rode and the girls got up behind the men. Indeed, the ponies had the road to themselves, for it was not safe for anything else. Shoremen and hillmen were speeding in the same direction. Bawneens and coats flew and flip-flapped in the wind.

"Half the road, you boor," shouted a hillman, riding a black colt to a shoreman on a white steed.

The only answer he got back was a crack of the whip

on the rump of Snowy and a loud yelp— "Hurrah for the shore!"

When the procession reached Paudeen's house, there was a céad míle fáilte before all. Some of the neighbors had been there all day putting the place in order for the wedding. On the day before, all the ovens in the village were kept busy baking bulogs and raisin bread. The Islanders wished to make a good impression on the mountaineers. This day was kept like a holiday! The men dressed in their best homespuns, and the women had on their multicolored shawls and bright red petticoats.

It was a beautiful evening. The sun nearing the west gleamed as if overheated from the trip across the dome of heaven. Now it sank into the liquid gold of the sea, but the afterglow still reflected in the cove below as the dark of night began to mix with the light of day. Paudeen's house started to fill from wall to wall, and later on the loft in the rear held the young lads with their feet dangling over the edge.

Though Paudeen was shiftless he was a gentle neighbor, which persuaded most of the villagers to give him wedding presents. Mickileen Liam brought him a fine mahogany chair that he had found ashore many years before. Old Coilin gave a glass candlestick that had been in the family for generations. Little Nan presented Paudeen with a beautiful picture of Saint Patrick driving the snakes out in the sea. Luke son-of-Old-Paudeen gave him a woven basket shaped like a cradle and made of peeled osiers, which might be useful some day. The Changeling himself brought a duck and a drake. Even Martin O'Cooney gave a present: a fine shillelagh to peace-loving Paudeen.

Little Nan and Sally were busy now preparing the wedding supper. There was fine yeast and buttermilk oven-bread. Some of the bulogs were of a golden hue from egg yolks and speckled with raisins and currants. There was choice mutton and bacon galore; pollack, cod, haddock, sole and lobsters, too. The tables were set in the parlor, and when one group had dined another sat in. Wine and punch were special for the ladies and served around.

"Slainte to ye all, my dear friends," toasted Paudeen. "And may we all be seven thousand times better in health and happiness this time twelve-month."

"Good health to yourself and to your lovely bride and the best of luck and happiness. May ye live on and on until ye see your children's children and the fourth generation," chorused the house with the tinkling of the glasses.

"Twang, twang," from the violin as the fiddler sawed with his bow and tightened the strings to put the instrument in tune. A space was kept clear in the middle of the floor for the dancers. The musician played a lively reel. Paudeen jumped up like a cat, caught his bride around the waist and swung her around. Soon the floor was full of lads and lassies capering and weaving in and out. Now they swung around in a swirling mass, and none could tell which was lad or lass. The rustling of the petticoats and the wind from bawneens and coats flying above their heads fanned the fire into a blaze, and the big kettle hanging over it started to sing.

"Beat a foot on it, a chara. Good lad, swing her again."

The Changeling hit the floor hard with his boot ending that swing and pitched his cap in the air. "Hurrah, hurrah. Up Muighinis."

"Heh, heh, heh," cackled O'Cooney.

In the changing of partners now there was a weaving in and out, backward and forward, and a stamping of feet.

The dancers hit the floor hard with a tat-tat-tat at the end of a bar.

"We'll have a song now. Come on, Luke, and give us a stave. Raise up your heart, a chara."

As Luke cleared his throat, there was clapping of hands.

Oh, Nelly Bawn my sweet colleen and true love of my
    heart,
Let me lay my hand on you, or from this life I'll depart.
I'd swim the wide Suir and the lovely Shannon after thee,
 Tis yourself that took the sway from the lassies of
    Loughrea.

"God be with you forever, Luke," and a clapping of hands.

Martin son-of-Anna went around now with a cruis-keen and glasses to serve the uisge-beatha, the water of life. A hillman and a shoreman were out on the floor beating time to a hornpipe and trying hard to tire each other out. Sweat glistened on the faces of the rival dancers.

All of a sudden the music stopped, for a fight was brewing at the back door.

"There was never a boat built that could beat the *May-flower*," shouted Sean Fada, a tall slender athlete.

"How you talk without rhyme or reason," roared Lia-meen Toby, a short slim dandy from the hills. "Do you remember the Clochronta Regatta?"

"Wasn't I myself the sheetrope man in the *Mayflower*? We won by the clever strategy of Jennings, the pilot, by making a shortcut inside the breaker of the Split Rock," said Sean.

"That shortcut was not fair, and you call it strategy."

"Strategy or no strategy, the *Mayflower* came in ahead of five others, winning the Clochronta Regatta," shouted Sean. "What in the devil do you know about pucans?"

"More than you," roared Liameen. "The Caisil pucan was by right the winner of the Clochronta races."

"Liar."

"Say that again. I dare you."

"You will, eh? You are a fool, too. Want to make anything out of that, little man?" challenged Sean.

Liameen jumped up and down and peeled off his coat, shouting, "Come out here on the fair play and my soul from the devil but——"

Sean threw off his bawneen, put two fingers inside his shirt collar, ripped open the breast and the buttons flew in all directions.

The whole house sprang to its feet trying to separate the fighters. There was shouting, jostling and pushing.

"Now, me lads, have a spark of sense. Sit down, sit down, will ye? There, there. Silence for a song."

The first blow from Sean knocked Liameen on his rear. Luke and Mickileen took a hold of Sean. Then the little man got up at once, raging to be let at the enemy.

"Raise it up, Coilin, give us a stave of *Una Bhan*. Silence for a song now."

Coilin cleared his throat and started: "A Una Bhan, a——"

Some ruffian fired a sod of turf and smashed the lamp hanging on the wall, plunging the house into darkness. Women screamed. In the hubbub, a bed crashed to the floor with the weight of people on it. There was a rush for the open door. The Changeling was shouting for order when someone pushed a sharp pin in his buttock. He yelled, jumped around, grabbed a chair, swung it over his head and smashed it against the wall. He held on to the leg and flailed around until he hit Mickileen Liam in the back of the head. Mickileen roared, groping around in the darkness until a candlestick on the bottom of the dresser came under his hand. He swung it, but it was snatched from him and pitched out through the window. The crashing of glass gave some the idea that a stone had come from the outside. In their mad surge the crowd carried the door and the frame with them.

Shouts and curses were interwoven with the sounds of falling walls while the tipsy gang chased one another through the fields and back-and-forth to the shore. Luke and the Changeling, though not peelers, were looking for Liameen and Sean Fada everywhere. After a careful search, the Changeling clapped his open hand on this man's shoulder, saying softly, "Is it here you are, a chara?" He wished to make sure of his prey in the dark.

"Who in the devil are you?" was shouted back. That was all, for he knew the voice of one of the disturbers.

He knocked the little man down with a right to the jaw, propped him up once more against a boulder and put him out cold. Then he pitched him over a wall to sleep in a bed of briars and thistles. But the Changeling was wise enough not to find Sean. Where was he now?

Sean had slipped quietly out a few minutes before, along with Molly Bawn, a buxom blonde. He led her through the yard to the bohreen and made for the sand dunes by the sea. Talk did not come easy with the throbbing of their hearts.

"Are you afraid of the fairies, Molly?"

"Not at all, a stór. I would go to the very end of the world with you," she whispered caressingly.

"Let's rest a while on this mossy mound in the shadow of the dune, Molly, mo gradh."*

"How bright the stars are, Sean, yet it is so lonely and dark here in the shelter of the sand dune," running her fingers through his thick hair.

Not a word was spoken for a long time. Their eyes shone and lips flew to lips as she snuggled up close in his arms.

Back in the house, Paudeen with a few helpers had a candle lit and was trying to clear away the wreckage. "Oh, I am ruined, the fine bed broken. Where will we sleep at all?" he moaned. "See the nice chair Mickileen gave me." Indeed, the chair was useful for the fire only. Some of the snakes from Saint Patrick's picture were found under the bed when Luke and Paudeen put the frame in place.

The wedding guests were on their way home now, and their singing could be heard along the road. A few lay stretched out under the hedges, lulled to sleep by the fumes of the barley juice. Right near the center of the village was the Geese Pond, from where the fields and a winding bohreen ran down the slope.

O'Cooney was staggering down this lane taking its two sides with him. He fell down and rolled into the middle of the lane. He raised his hands in the air and began to talk to himself: May the devil choke you for blocking the fine bohreen! You have drink taken. What is the good for any priest or bishop giving you advice? Advice wasted on a pig.

As he was reciting every detail, it dawned on him that he was mad at himself. He managed to crawl over to a stone, picked it up to kill himself. But it slipped from his grasp and rolled harmlessly down in a drain. Then he found a wisp of grass, gripped it firmly in his hand, and striking

* *Mo gradh:* My love

himself in the head with it, cried out, "You drunk, you good for nothing. Where will you go on the last day?" He rose to his standing with a deal of trouble and struck his legs with the grass until he fell and rolled into a ditch. There he lay stretched in the mud, groaning.

Next morning, on meeting Martin O'Cooney in the boh-reen, Mickileen whined, "It was a good enough night only for those fools who started to fight. I have a bump as big as a goose's egg on the back of my head. Some ruffian hit me in the dark."

"I can't hear you, for my head is split open and I am dead from the waist down," returned Martin.

"Arrah, what in the world at all is the matter with you?" asked Mickileen, bepuzzled and looking his friend up and down. "You are drenched with muddy water!"

"I can't hear you at all, a chara. But I am on my way now to find out has Paudeen any drop at all left."

"Don't disturb them, Martin," Mickileen interrupted. "Can't you remember that Paudeen is just married and along with his woman now? Come along with me, a chara, for I have a flask at home."

"I don't remember anything at all, a stór, but I can hear you well now," smiled Martin, shaking a shower of muddy water out of his clothes and turning on his heels to follow his friend.

Martin son-of-Anna, a husky middle-aged man, soon got the notion that it was time for him to find a woman. But he deemed it indelicate to bring her into the thatched white-washed cottage where he lived with his mother and younger brother.

"It wouldn't be hard for me to find a suitable girl if I had a house of my own," he said one night as they were sitting around the kitchen fire.

"Well, son," the mother replied, "I'd never be in your way, but your brother will be looking out for himself some day, too."

The latter, who was younger and well-knit, stood up and spoke. "I see no way out of it but to build a house. Coming on now toward winter we won't be so busy, and we could spend a part of the day quarrying stones."

Mother and sons picked the site for the new house on a height overlooking the sea. Would it not be easy galore to bring a boatload of well-shaped stones here from Duck Island and sand aplenty for the mortar in the strand nearby? That evening they measured the ground for the new house: forty feet long, sixteen feet wide and eight feet high. In those remote parts it is a custom to place stone marks at each of the four corners of a new building site three nights in succession for fear that the "Good People" might have a path there.

As the golden sun sank in the western sea, Martin laid three small stones on top of each other, saying, "In the name of the Father, and of the Son and of the Holy Ghost. Amen."

"The Fairies have no claim whatsoever to this spot," announced the mother on the third morning when they found the stones at each corner untouched. "My blessing to ye, sons."

The brothers grasped their spades and began to strip naked the backside of a hillock. Then again, they threw the spades away and used the crowbars to put a face on the work.

"It looks as if we might find some stones here," remarked Martin, turning loose a flat stone. Flags were back to back like the leaves of a book needing only the taste of the crowbar to tumble them out. Paud made heaps of them on the level outside.

"Ah, the fine lump that is asleep here in the dark for ages is going to help me."

As he dug them out, Martin chatted with each. "Musha, my well-shaped slab of pure granite, you are just needed by myself to build a new home."

If a stone was too heavy, he kindled a fire on it right in the quarry, which split it into even lumps. Though the two worked much harder than if a ganger was over them, yet they were as light as starlings walking home in the evening.

At long last the quarry grew stubborn, and the brothers had to try their strength and skill with the wedge and hammer.

"Could we find some dynamite anywhere?" whispered the brother, taking the curve out of his back.

"Dynamite indeed!" sneered the other. "You should know that is out while the damn Union Jack flies over us."

"God bless the work, men," saluted Old Coilin, who was just then passing up the bohreen. "Going to build?"

"A new house," added Martin in a jovial mood. "When it is finished, I'll find a woman right away to put into it."

"Find the woman first, a chara. Then you can build the house at your ease," advised Coilin.

"Have a spark of sense, man. I need only to beckon one when the new home is ready."

"My teeth have grown twice, so have yours. Do you remember what the old proverb says: Nor house nor castle wins a maid, but some kind of silly strategy. Call it love if you wish."

"Nonsense," laughed Martin, taking up his sledge, as the latter walked on.

"There are nice flat stones embedded in the strand," suggested the brother. "We could dig them up when the tide is out."

"The rapid flow of the Spring tide will not allow us time to split the large ones by kindling a fire on them. But what we should do is tie a chain around a big one at low ebb and fasten the end of it in the boat. When she swims, her buoyancy will lift the rock and we can row into shallower water," said Martin, taking the chain out of the boat.

"A good plan," agreed Paud, digging around a boulder with his spade to make a place for the chain to hold. "These stones are not like others found around here."

"Nor should they be," replied Martin, who was putting the loop of the chain around a stone. "This is part of the ballast that was in the big Swedish barque wrecked here long ago, and this strand is called Swedish Strand ever since."

The sun was an oar's length above the hill in the east, pointing its crimson bars into many a home, as if trying to rouse up the lazy sleepers. The wind had vanished, and drops from the eaves and the sunbeams danced merrily on the placid surface of the cove. Indeed, it was a balmy morning, and the brothers took the pucan and sailed the twelve miles to Aran for a load of limestone. Pictures of fish, crabs, lobsters and shellfish may be clearly seen on the bluish-white slabs of limestone. A big cod with his mouth wide open as if he had been caught in mud that had hardened instantly. Those queer etchings are often found three hundred feet above the sea level, which proves beyond a doubt that Aran was once under the sea. In the evening, they returned home with a light westerly and landed at the pier.

When everything was ready, Martin asked Old Paudeen to break the limestones small. He was a good hand at it. Being a Revolutionary most of his life, he had spent long terms in British prisons where he broke heaps and heaps of stones for road mending. The small limestones could be burned and mixed with black turf in a kiln at night so that there would be lime aplenty for the mortar.

Big Mat, the stonemason, came the following week. Martin, who was handy with stones, helped the builder, while his brother mixed the lime and sand and handed the granite stones and mortar to the builders. The walls and gables rose little by little as time passed, until one evening the crow stone was embedded in a few trowelfuls of mortar atop the sharp-pointed gable.

Then the brothers went to the mountain to cut scraws on the marsh with spades and sedge in the glen with sickles. Pitch pine logs that they had found ashore the winter before were raised from the strand at the dead of night while the peelers were asleep. The wood was sawed into rafters, laths and beams in the moonlight. After the scraws had been laid on the rafters, the brothers could work inside on the rainy day or with the lamplight at night to lay floors and plaster walls. When the first fire was kindled on the hearth, the brothers divided the six acres of land.

The birds sang gaily this evening as Martin was pacing up and down in the bohreen like a sentry on guard. He was between two minds in trying to decide which of two girls would be his wife. At last he leaned on the garden wall to think. He noticed that the infant rye was coming up nicely in the field. Had it not the heavy dew at night and sunshine by day to nurse the dark clay with vigor enough to push up the new life? The snails who had slept in the old stone walls for the past six months were awakened now, starving with the hunger and already trimming the green mantle of rye blades a couple of feet out from the wall.

"My soul from the devil, but ye are clever," said Martin to himself, as he watched the busy snails carrying loads of young rye into the old wall. "Arrah, it's no use arguing with myself any longer," spitting at a snail that was cutting a blade of rye. He hurried down the bohreen and never stopped until he saluted into Darach Mor's house. Martin made a sign to Darach to come outside, glancing at a village woman who was sitting on the hob.

"Well, a chara," whispered Martin as they leaned against the gable end.

"Would you come along with me some night soon to go asking for a woman? My new house is ready for her now."

"I wish you the best of luck, Martin. Where do you intend to go?"

"To John son-of-Dara. I think his daughter, Brighid, would make a good and sensible wife."

"The buxom beauty of the hills," gasped the other, emitting a low whistle and looking Martin in the eye.

"She'll be mighty glad to find the offer. Everyone knows by now about my fine new house."

"Too good you are for the best of them, but——" he flattered shrewdly, gazing out to sea. "I'll go along with you, of course, and welcome, Martin."

This evening was a kind of chilly when Martin saluted into Darach's again. The naked necks of bottles peeking out of his coat pockets gave his mission away before he had opened his mouth. Sonny son-of-Tom and Darach were sitting on stools at the fire smoking their pipes.

"Wet your lips," Martin warmly invited, standing the bottles of poteen on the table.

"It is a good drop. It holds the beads," Sonny assured. "Where did you find it?"

"In Dirrane's, Leitermulan village across the bay. I bought twenty gallons for the wedding and all——killing two birds with the one stone."

Sonny glanced over at Darach, wishing to say a word about counting the chickens, but instead he said boldly, "Now, what are we waiting for, boys?"

Darach rose to his standing, yawned and said a kind of absent-minded, "Have you any other place in mind, a chara, besides Eoin's?"

"Am I going to marry two?" growled Martin.

"Not at all, Martin," replied Darach, winking at Sonny.

Soon the sails were hoisted on the pucan, and with the fair west wind it did not take long to reach Crumpaun Pier on the mainland. After mooring the boat, each had a mouthful of the barley juice and then began to shorten the road.

Eoin's house was quiet, for they had been in bed for hours. A big dog ran out from the back of the barn, barking. Darach knocked on the door. A window was raised upstairs and a head came out and a sleepy voice asked who was there.

"Me," replied Darach, looking up at the head.

"And who are you?"

"Darach."

"Darach what?"

"Darach Mor from the Island of Muighinis."

The door was opened and the trio saluted in. To be sure, the man of the house was puzzled as he did not know from Heaven above what had taken those men to his house at such an untimely hour. He found chairs and the strangers sat down.

"Was it looking for some lost sheep ye were, or——"

"A woman," added Darach. "We came here to you to-night, a chara, to ask your daughter, Brighid, for Martin son-of-Anna, God bless this house and everyone in it."

By now all the family had gathered around the fire. Drinks were served in regular order as Darach and Sonny took turns praising Martin. Yet, there seemed to be an overhanging cloud of gloom.

Indeed, the daughter was pretty. The shining blackness of her thick locks like a raven's wing reached to her slim waist. Her figure was tall and slender and her eyes were a sparkling blue.

"Is there any hope at all for us?" asked Darach, after he had said his say and sat down.

"Well," replied the man of the house dryly, "we are not to say yes or no, but——"

"But," interrupted the pale-faced wife, "but our Brighid is not going to be tied down to the world yet; thus it is not fair to lead ye on."

"No hope, men," added Eoin, with a shrug of his shoulders.

"Come on, lads," shouted Darach, a ring of vexation in his voice.

"Where will we go now?" asked Sonny as they walked on toward the shore.

Poor Martin was silent. He had not been prepared for this abrupt refusal, and the dagger-thrust to his pride stunned him. But at last he muttered thickly, "If ye can come along with me tomorrow night, we'll try somewhere else."

"That's the right spirit, a chara," consoled Darach, trying to temper the fire of hidden anguish around Martin's heart. "Never you fear, Martin, we'll be with you to the very end, come what may. Indeed, there is as good a fish in the sea yet as was ever caught."

In short, the trio searched all over the parish in the weeks to come, but all in vain. Now it was common gossip among the old women about this one and that one who had refused Martin. The gossips were in their glory to have the yarns for spinning.

This night the ground was baked hard with frost which sounded from the tramping of the night visitors going home. The faint wind did not disturb the quietness. Gray mists hung over the fields, and the lapwing piped now and again down near the pond in the glen. Sonny, Darach and Martin were so tired that they had to sit down at the ditch to rest, think and discuss their next maneuver.

"Wherever we go, let's leave the poteen outside until we feel our way inside at first. If we keep going on as we are feeding the whole parish, the twenty gallons will run dry even before we can find the colleen," counseled Darach. "Didn't you pay ten shillings a gallon for it?"

"True," replied Martin in a sad tone.

"I told you before to try Tom son-of-Micky, but you wouldn't give an ear."

"The daughter is not good looking, but she is strong and

a splendid worker. Good looks never boiled a pot, a chara. But when you put out the light and you snug in bed with her and——" Darach whispered cautiously. "What do you say, stubborn?"

Poor Martin felt now as if millions of tiny worms were gnawing at his brain making his thinking confused just like a dream. At last he mumbled, "Ah, but the world is gone to the house of the Devil, when I stoop so low as——"

"Let's be going in the name of God," interrupted Sonny, rising to his standing and stretching himself.

"Lift up your heart, Martin," encouraged Darach. "Think of all the brave men who came before you. But above all don't forget about Biddy and how you will be kept warm and thrilled in her arms next winter."

Before going into Tom's house for the matchmaking, they hid the two bottles of poteen in the mouth of the turf stack. The people of the house were up yet, but it is little they had hoped for visitors calling on such a mission. After the usual talks, Darach asked for the daughter, Biddy, for Martin, and it seemed to be fair sailing. Biddy was a strong healthy woman in her late thirties with thick dark hair and a light fuzz growing on her upper lip.

While the matchmaking was going on in Tom's, O'Cooney, who lived nearby, was finding the Devil from his woman for not borrowing a basket of turf somewhere before the night. Himself had a load of turf on the mainland pier, but he overslept in the mornings and missed the full tides. "Have a little patience, a stór, and I'll find a few sods. Didn't Tom, next door, tell me not to be scarce while he had any?"

In a short time, O'Cooney was filling his basket in Tom's rick. On feeling a bottle under his hand, his heart jumped for he thought it was a trap! "Maybe the turf was being stolen and Tom wished to scare the thief. Dynamite!" he said to himself, walking backwards and throwing a few sods at the bottle. But nothing at all happened. He shuffled carefully over and peered at the thing in the semidarkness. It was a bottle. He rubbed his fingers on the cork and, finding the smell of poteen, pulled the cork and tasted it, then laid it gently in his basket. He started to throw more turf in his basket and found another bottle. "My soul from the devil, but there might be more," he whispered to himself, pitching the turf this way and that way until he heard Tom's door open and hurried away. Not alone did he have fuel for the fire, but mountain dew to warm the cockles of his heart for many a day.

"Go on out and bring that in," whispered Darach to Martin when everything was settled.

"Oh, God and Mary," moaned Martin as he searched. "But not a taste of it is left. Some rogue must have seen us hiding it there."

"Where are the poteen bottles?" asked Sonny in sudden alarm when Martin came back empty-handed.

"Gone."

"We had a few bottles of poteen hid in the mouth of the turf stack and they are stolen," Darach explained, turning over to Tom.

"Some ruffian was stealing your turf, too," added Martin defensively.

"It is all scattered here and there."

"I'll scatter ye," interrupted Tom in a storm of anger. "Whoever heard before of any decent Christian looking for a girl without a drop! Ye have some fine excuse. Here, here now, get a fast move on," glaring at Martin as he opened the door. "Out of my house quick, ye pack of stingy misers."

The door was slammed shut so close to Martin's heels that he stumbled and fell with the excitement and sprained his ankle.

"Wasn't that the bad luck when all was settled," whispered Sonny with a deep sigh as they carried Martin home.

"Everything was going our way. The fat goose that Biddy herself had killed in our honor," added Darach.

"I think myself that it was a gander the way it honked on seeing the glistening sharp knife. The poor girl was so excited that she grabbed the first bird that came under her hand in the dark barn," chuckled Sonny behind Martin's back.

"Ah, friends of my heart," wailed Martin. "Don't ye be making fun of me now. I'm badly hurt in more ways than one. But one thing, I'm through with the women forever."

I often helped the poor man to thatch his house. Years passed by, and the time came when the misfortunes of life were so heavy that the care of one house was enough. The new house was left there, and in a short time the sunbeams poured down through the roof and danced on the floor while the crows cawed insultingly as they flew in and out through the broken windows.

A wet summer came and the turf did not dry, causing misery aplenty in many a shore dweller's home. The following winter the pitch pine rafters and beams of the new house were cut down and burned as fuel to keep the brothers warm, as the mother had passed away to her reward. In the course of time, Martin's brother married a girl from the mainland, and he stayed along with them in the old house. Indeed, they were honest and hard-working men who were out on the Atlantic late and early.

The walls and sharp-pointed gables of the new house are still standing, but poor Martin himself is making clay. May dear God be good to his soul and the souls of the faithful departed from the Island of Muighinis.

During the long winter nights, I used to visit the homes of the old storytellers and listen to the Gaelic songs and stories that had been handed down from father to son for generations. The notion came to me then to write them down on paper as they came from the lips of the seanachaidhe.*

In 1919, English soldiers and peelers raided our home, taking, among other things, my collection of folklore. Doubtless they thought that the Gaelic script contained the secrets of the Sinn Fein movement, myself happening to be the president at the time. Losing the folklore took the wind out of my sails, but I kept on writing stories out of my own head and sending them to a Gaelic magazine called the *Stoc*, or *Trumpet*. This monthly had a long period of useful existence until the printing press was destroyed by the Black and Tans and the printers themselves killed or put in prison. Even after this magazine was dead, I kept on writing short stories about the sea and hiding them in tin boxes buried in the sand for fear the militia would raid us again.

Indeed, the fear had been instilled in me from my early years while attending the national school set up at the expense of the Irish taxpayer. The teachers knew not one word of Gaelic, while the pupils knew the Gaelic only. I remember the big red-faced inspector who came all the way from England to examine us. He had to sit on two chairs for one was too scarce for his behind. He roared at

* *seanachaidhe:* storyteller

us because we did not understand him. Then he ordered the class to write a short story about His Majesty.

This is what I put down on my sheet of paper:

His Majesty is a gray rock out in the sea where the people fish. A black cormorant stands on his head and she goes for a fish, comes back again and dirties on His Majesty and goes to sleep. His Majesty is there for a long time and the black cormorant leaves him and goes away with the white gull with the black back.

When he read my story, he closed his mouth tight and glared at me. "Tchick, tchick," he said, tearing up my composition and throwing it into my face. Then he turned to the teacher, scolded her in English, took up his black bag and waddled out through the open door to the jaunting car waiting for him.

That night the neighbors came visiting to our house as usual, and Old Paudeen asked me, "Musha, what did you learn today, Jimeen?"

"We had the big English inspector in the school and he told us to write a story on His Majesty. But when I handed him mine he flew into a rage, tore it up and flung it in my face. He was very angry at the teacher, too."

"And what did you put down?"

"I wrote about His Majesty, the rock."

The house burst out laughing and I wondered why.

"Arrah, Jimeen, you were lucky that he didn't kill you entirely, for it was the King of England he meant," chuckled Paudeen. "That rock which is named 'Mullannambhod'* in Gaelic is called "His Majesty" only in front of the women."

"Why is that?" I asked.

* *mullannambhod:* rock of male parts

"Wait for a few more years, and you'll learn—and not from your English teacher, either."

When I had grown up a little and got the loan of an English magazine from a returned Yank, I came across a piece that caught my attention. It offered a crown of money for the best essay about an unusual happening in any townland in Eire. Right then I got the urge to try my skill in the English. Five shillings in real money was worth it. But what would I write about?

There came to my mind then the story of the boat that was drowned on Saint McDara's feast day when the pilgrimage was changed from Saint McDara's Isle to Muighinis for the first time in thirteen hundred years. The story of this tragedy, which did happen on the sixteenth day of July, 1904, I knew well in the Gaelic. Was I not there myself as a small gossoon mingling with the crowd?

This bright morning I rose up at the break of day and hurried to the barn loft to write my story. The hens were cackling underneath, announcing to the world that they were about to lay fine fresh eggs. Daida began to call me, and I ran out in the meadow and pretended to pick up the small stones out of the grass. After breakfast was over, I went digging mold. Now and again I used to forget the spade work and wander into my story. That night I took a bundle of peeled rushes, matches and a few sheets of paper to the barn loft. My hideout was full of sweet smelling hay, boxes and sails. I closed the gable-end door, put a few rushes in an oil-filled scallop shell and lit them. Placing an empty soap box near the light, I smoothed out a sheet of paper and started to write down my story with a lead pencil. It was deep in the night when I finished. But the hardest work was still ahead, for now I must translate it from Gaelic into English. Nor would I have any spare time for that until Sunday, as we would be busy for the next four days bringing seaweed ashore from the wild rocks.

In the nights we planned to put new hooks on the spiller to replace the ones that were lost. Though I used no pencil, yet I was doing the translating in my mind while pulling the laminaria weed and tying the hooks.

This Sunday I was up at the dawn of day, so still and quiet that a wren's egg would not break under my foot lest I would wake up the house. I climbed the ladder to the barn loft with an English book under my arm. I worked hard all that day to make a rough translation. When it grew dark, I lit the rushes and read my essay aloud. Was it the queer sound of the foreign language falling on my ear, or did it need more polishing?

The next evening I trudged off to the gray-haired Yank and read my masterpiece to him. He gave me a willing hand in the correcting. It was deep that bright and calm night when I returned home, the stars above glistening like nails of silver and the lonely big sea murmuring from Long Strand.

At the end of the following week I had rewritten my story half a score of times. One night I nearly burned the barn as the lighted rushes fell from the box into the hay. Except for an old sail that I pitched on the flames to smother them, the barn would have been in ashes. Now the sweet fragrance of the new hay and clover was replaced by the smell of burnt wood and tar.

After much trouble, I had the story finished. Indeed, I had been so taken up with it while translating and writing that I spoke very little. This caused some of the villagers to whisper that I was not all there. Be that as it may, peace of mind came to me only when I had folded the manuscript, put it into an envelope and taken it to the post office.

From that day on my eyes were peeled watching for the postboy who visited our Island three days a week. I often crossed through the fields to meet him, saying, "Are you not a little late today, and, if you have any letters for us, I'll take them and save you the trip."

Three weeks had passed and I was giving up hope. One evening, coming home from the sea, I found a letter awaiting me. I picked it off the table, turning it round and round. My heart pounded like a triphammer. At last I took the bull by the horns and slit the edge of the envelope. A piece of bluish paper fell on the floor: a check for five shillings! Could it be true? It was! Soon the news went out that I had received a check from a publisher in the big town for a story I had written in English. As the news spread the money grew—first to a pound, and then there was no limit.

The villagers came to our house that night. I read them the letter thanking me and showed the check—not once but a score of times. As newcomers strayed in, Old Paudeen would look at me and nod, "Read that letter over again, Jimeen."

Next day the magazine arrived. That night the house was full to listen to the story of The Drowning read from the print itself. Silence reigned. If anyone stirred or coughed, Mickileen Liam would threaten with an outstretched hand. The cricket who started to chirp in the hob made Old Paudeen so angry that he spat at him and muttered a curse. After a time, I no longer had to do the translating, for Paudeen who sat on the hob all night, knew it by heart and could change it word by word into the Gaelic just as it was in "Ireland's Own" in the English.

"Musha Jimeen of my heart," one of the colleen visitors would exclaim from time to time, looking at me with eyes full of wonder, "but you must have a great head entirely, God bless you."

When my fame went out as a writer, I was often invited to a neighbor's house to write to a daughter or a son in a foreign land. On such occasions the best that was to be found in the house was mine. To be sure, the scribe who went around like this needs must shelter the secrets entrusted to him much the same as a priest with the confession.

Barbara daughter-of-Mickil came to our house this evening and said to me: "Jimeen, a stór, could you come along with me to write a letter to Sean?"

"Go along with the woman," ordered Mama, who was washing the dishes.

"Thank you very much," Barbara said, and she and myself walked out through the doorway.

When we reached her house down at the Point, she found a chair for me and set it at the head of the table.

"The notepaper and ink I have here, a stór," she said, laying them down next to me.

"What do you want me to write?" I asked, as I smoothed out the sheet of paper in front of me and dipped my pen in the ink.

"Read the old letter he sent and may God bless you," she said, sitting down on a chair beside me and pushing back the ringlets of her dark shiny hair under her headkerchief.

The letter went as follows:

My dear and loving Mother and Father:

I drop you these few lines hoping to find ye all in the

best of health as this note leaves myself at present, thanks be to God for His kind mercy to us all. I hope that the friends and neighbors are all well and that the weather is nice over there. How is Mickileen son-of-Liam, Old Paudeen, the Rover and all my old friends? Give my love to all the girls in the village.

Last summer was very hot here. Some poor devils got struck by the sun. For weeks on end there wasn't a puff of wind, just as if one was in the stomach of a cow and she stuck in a bog hole. The sweat ran out of my boots and I carrying the hod of mortar up to the fifth floor of the structure. May the Lord help every Christian in this wicked world.

There is no race in this country who have so much wealth as the Jews. They know how to make it and wise enough to hold on to it. But it is a great blessing that they are law-abiding and peaceful and never go near the saloons. None ever saw any of them real drunk or fighting either.

Dear parents, I haven't much more to say this time. Write soon to me again, and let me know all the news. Thank you so much for the package of dulse and the wrasse which I received last week. The dulse was very tasty and the sweet wrasse brought many happy memories back to me. I am sending you the sum of three pounds in this letter. Hoping you'll get it all right. Tell my father not to be too bold on the sea. I suppose the kelp is all burned by now and that ye are digging the spuds. I must finish this letter now and put it in the post office tonight. I hope to see ye all yet with the help of God.

> With blessing and love,
> from your loving son, Sean

"He hadn't much to say about his relatives over there, but that is the way he always was," Barbara commented, folding the letter.

"You may start right now, and it will be only a few lines. Indeed, you know yourself what to say better than I, for you have read his letter."

Barbara began to dictate:

My dear and loving son Sean:

I am writing to you these few lines hoping to find you in good health as this note leaves me at present, and all the neighbors as well as if I named them one by one, thanks be to God for His kind mercy to us all. I received your most welcome letter a week ago. We are all glad to hear from you—that you are well and happy, thank the Lord. May God bless you and save you for the three pounds which we badly needed to help pay the rent. The agent was barking at me before I got your letter. His bark was growing into a growl and a summons to the court. May the money not increase or profit the schemer of a landlord, the English Colonel Nolan, a tyrant which high and mighty bishops propped up in the last election. There is no change at all in this poor place. When I sold the pig at the Fair of Cashel last month, I gave a few shillings to the priest to have a Mass said for your grandmother's soul.

Aside to me, she said, "You know, Jimeen, His Reverence has grown somewhat childish from the age, God help us all. He takes snuff and has the bosom of his fine new vest spoiled with the stuff. Well, you may start on the letter again.

"I pray to God and to the Blessed Virgin that you will have good luck in America. It is a land that makes up a few which will be heard about, but it ruins many more and not a word at all about them. Don't forget to say your prayers, for they say that's a wicked country. Take good care of yourself and keep away from the drink for it does destroy Gaels galore. A letter has just come to the village saying that John son-of-Martin was killed by the train. Watch out for the train, for the sun, too, and also for the snake.

To me in an aside, Barbara remarked, "I heard Mickileen son-of-Liam saying that if the snake puts his eye on you, your bread is eaten. The devilish thing makes a wheel out of himself, holding the tip of his tail in his mouth to whistle, and then goes like the March wind."

"I also heard Mickileen saying," I added, "that he had a good job once out in the forest felling trees, but when a snake twisted herself around the neck of his comrade and sucked his blood, himself got so scared that he ran away and tramped the long white dusty roads to Baltimore, where he went to sea aboard a scallop boat, dredging."

"To be sure, it was a good thing that Saint Patrick drove the devils out of this country, with his stick and Book," she broke in." But, Jimeen, tell Sean now:

You know Mairin Mhike, who went to the old school with you, son. She got married to some kind of a doctor who the Government sent over from England to look into a potato disease! Whoever heard of a potato being sick? They had the wedding and the Christening in one sweep and galore mountain dew for a whole week. I don't know in the world how can she make him out for he knows not a word of Gaelic.

"Jimeen, strange things do happen when those English come over to us. Gossip says that he grabbed her first in the thick smoke of a kelp kiln, and she bringing in the weed from the stack to the burners. Mairin herself might be no good, but may he burn in hell, God save us."

She continued with the letter:

We have a mountain of trouble here, God help us. Galore of the boys were put into concentration camps for being in the Irish Volunteers. It is the English again. May the seven red devils take them to the lower depths of hell.

Sean Mor found death, may God have mercy on his soul. Ah, the poor creature had a strong shout in his day. He had a big funeral and plenty of poteen was served at the wake.

Not much vigor is left on Old Kathleen now. Not a tooth is left in her head. Yet, it would do your heart good to watch her eating a boxty cake. Her gums are as hard as granite. And for that matter nothing is wrong with her tongue, either. Old Mickil son-of-Marc passed away about a month ago. His breath and soul were in a flutter the week before, trying out who would be the first to go. But the blessing of God was on him to depart when he did. Mo lein! but that is the day that makes no lie, and we all must go. Myself was at the wake and if I may say so, he had a decent enough passing.

Everyone here is much the same as you saw them. There was a big storm a few nights ago and O'Cooney's old house would be stripped naked, only for Old Paudeen and Micky Tom who managed to toss some ropes across the roof which held the scraws, for the thatch had gone with the wind.

Said Barbara to me in an aside: "Indeed, it was O'Cooney's own fault, the fool, for he never puts a hand to his home during the fine weather, but strutting around like a King keeping the rest of the villagers idle with his chitchat. Go ahead now with the letter, a stór."

It is not so bad here. Good prices are for kelp, carrigeen, and fish, and the potatoes grow good. Anyone who is not too lazy to eat will live. Maire Sally's cow, Speckles, had a fine calf, God bless them all. She brought a pail of the first milk to me, may the Lord increase her store.

Mickil, the man of the house, came in now with a basket of potatoes. After saluting me in a friendly manner, he glanced at what I had put down.

"Read what you have written until he hears it," his wife commanded, handing me a few more sheets of notepaper.

He listened to me nodding his head and stroking his bushy dark mustache. When I had finished, he smiled and said, "Very good indeed, may God spare you the health. But a chara, you did not mention the fishing at all."

"Tell the boy what to put down. It's not too late yet."

"He knows better himself than I what to say about fishing. Tell him that it was a good year in the Sciarda Rocks. And also on the Big Breakers. We brought two thousand wrasse and the same count of cod, haddock and pollack from those wild places. A dead whale was washed ashore here a week ago. He is sixty feet long and as thick as a

~ 181 ~

hooker. We don't know from heaven above what is best for us to do, but we must do something soon. Not a bit of wrack came ashore yet, but the wind don't stay long enough in the right direction and——"

"Don't talk nonsense like that to put into a letter," Barbara interrupted, and her dark eyes lit up with the impatience.

"Indeed, it is of more import than Speckles having a calf. Everyone knows that while well-fed bulls are idling on the Island, cows will have calves. Can't you see how excited the shore-dwellers get when a barrel of rum or a bale of cotton is washed in because the people don't expect them; but a cow having a calf . . ." he chuckled, winking at me.

"Tell Sean, a stór," she broke in, "that your own people are well and that you yourself wrote this letter, that Mickil and myself are sending him our love and blessing. We both of us pray to God to protect him in that far-away city. With love galore from his mother and father. P.S. Mickileen Liam still steers his gleotog out to the fishing bank. He is in his glory on the sea and I do think the poor man would be lonesome even in Heaven without his boat. Love from Mama and Daida."

Said the couple as with one voice when I had finished, "May you be seven thousand times better this time twelve-month, Jimeen."

"The same blessing to ye," I replied, folding the sheets and putting them inside the envelope.

One fine evening, on coming home from the fishing bank and myself finished with school, I found Colm O'Gaora, may dear God be good to his soul, waiting for me. Colm was an active fighter for independence, also an organizer for the Gaelic language.

"Jimeen," said he, after we had talked about this and that for a while. "Would you find any fault in going to a Gaelic College for a month to find some knowledge about the tricks of the teacher? Would you like to be a Gaelic teacher in the English-speaking parts of the country?"

Red weed galore was coming ashore as the kelp-making and fishing season had just started. That was my way of life then as it was for all the Islanders. Yet when my own people agreed, I gave my consent to Colm there and then. It flashed through my mind that I would be much like the Holy Monk who had sailed from our shore in the far distant past to teach the true religion to the heathen of other lands.

On a bright morning in the month of June, I packed my bag ready to leave. The villagers came to our house to bid me good-bye.

"Great is the luck that is on you, Jimeen, to leave the kelp-making and fishing behind you," said Mickileen Liam, shaking my hand warmly.

"A chara," smiled the Rover, slapping me on the back, "You might marry a fine colleen and settle down on a farm out in the rich lands of Meath far away from the sound of the sea."

The sparrows chirped in the eaves and the lark sang loud and high as I walked down to the pier along with the neighbors. My mother kissed me a tearful good-bye on the quay. Then I boarded the pucan. Our dog, Watch, seemed to sense that I was going away, for he raced along the strand howling as we sailed down the bay. The wind was fresh and fair from the west when we landed in the City of Galway. That night I slept in the boat along with my father and brother, Kieran.

"We'll go over to the railroad station with you," said Daida next morning after having our breakfast in the boat.

"I'm very lonesome for home," I sobbed as we stood on the platform waiting for the train to come in.

"You are only going to the next county, son, and you'll be back home again in a month's time with the help of God," smiled Daida.

I bade good-bye to both and boarded the train for Ballinarobe, County Mayo.

I was never away from home before for more than one day at a time. Lying in bed that first night in the village of Tournmakeady was more than I could bear, turning and tossing and thinking of my people at home. At the break of day when I had the pillow drenched with my tears, I fell into a troubled sleep.

I was up with the lark that lovely morning. "Cuckoo, cuckoo" and there was herself on the gable end of an old monastry. The corncrake with his own harsh cry was down in the meadow. I was lodging in a thatched whitewashed cottage on the shore of Lough Mask. The Gaelic College was nearby on the cheek of a hill, and I walked there this first day to enroll in the advanced class.

When school hours were over, the lads took the girls out sailing on the lake and often landed on small islands where we had picnics. That month slipped away all too quickly for me, and I was lonely again—but this time from parting with those light-hearted Gaelic scholars to return to my home in the west.

November came around again, and the fishing season was in full swing. Here I was now sailing out to sea at dawn and coming back at dusk with the boat loaded down with cod, haddock, pollack and wrasse. On arriving home from the sea one evening I found a letter offering me a position as a teacher of Gaelic in County Roscommon at a salary of three pounds a week. Was I the happy man then!

On a sunshiny morning with a light southerly I sailed in the pucan once more to Galway, along with Daida and my younger brother, Sean. Early the next morning, I boarded a train for Boyle, County Roscommon, and lodged there for the night. Was I not an old dog on the road now?

Next day, I strolled into a barber's shop to have a haircut. The barber, a stocky man with a blotchy face, looked at me sourly and said nothing.

"A haircut, if you please," said I, trying to act casual. He only grunted and began clipping my hair. In a few moments, he stopped.

"Pay me now for cutting off your mop of curly hair," he said. "I need the money right away."

It was my first time in a barber's shop and, thinking it the custom, I handed him a silver crown. He pocketed it and walked out the door. Upon returning, he paid me no attention.

"The haircut is only fourpence. Please give me back the change," I asked him.

"Don't bother me or my soul from the devil, but I'll——" he roared, grabbing a razor and swinging it around my head. "Did you see the colors in that rainbow?"

he chuckled, picking up a scissor and snapping off one of my eyebrows.

I rose to my standing at once and ran to the street with my hair half cut, an eyebrow lost and my silver crown gone. Then I hailed a jaunting car and told the driver to take me to John Mulvihill's in the village of Carroreigh where I was going to stay.

On my arrival at Mulvihill's the dinner was just ready, for they had been expecting me. Now, I would not give a drop of blood with the shame. A teacher from the West coming to such respectable people looking like a drunken tinker. I pulled my cap down tightly in front and back. The house put a welcome before me and invited me to sit in at the table. Mary, who was John's sister, sat on the chair next to me, glancing now and again at the back of my head to find out if the cap was glued on.

John, who sat opposite me, broke the silence. "Would you say the grace before meals in the Gaelic, Jim?"

I looked over at the man of the house, who with his hands clasped and half-shut eyes, was looking up at the ceiling; Mary, her hands folded across her breast and her neat brown-haired head bowed. Miss Shanley, the cook, slender and tall, stood like a statue with a dish of smoking ham in her hand and she trying to watch me through the fingers of the other hand.

Just then Kelly, the English teacher who lodged there, darkened the doorway. He stood still to watch us.

The sweat was rolling off my face in rills. I snapped off my cap baring a hot smoking head. Miss Shanley smiled, laying the dish in the center of the table. I said the Grace in Gaelic and my voice a little shaky. Then we started to eat and I told of my trip to the barber in Boyle, how he had kept my crown, cut my eyebrow and only half my hair.

"You were lucky," chuckled Kelly. "I know him very well. You're not the first he mistreated and cut up with a knife."

"You should never wear a cap," smiled Mary, "you have such lovely golden curls."

Kelly, a tall dark-haired young man, found the scissors, cut the rest of my hair and trimmed the eyebrow to match the other. Was I thankful to him!

I shall always remember the villages of Callow and Ballanamina on the shores of Lough Gara where I taught Gaelic two nights a week. This body of fresh water was about seven miles from Boyle, County Roscommon. Often myself was invited by the kind and gentle people to their homes, where I was treated like a Bishop. Most of the peasants held only a few acres of land that their ancestors had reclaimed from the bogs. Right at their doorsteps were broad fertile plains and rolling hills stretching as far as the eye could see. But alas! Those rich lands were not for keeping the people alive, but were for fattening bullocks and sheep to feed the British Army, to conquer new lands and kill the natives.

Lough Gara had once been a pleasant fertile valley where the people lived in contentment. Then a giant landlord came from the north and evicted all the tenants for no reason at all. There was a fine spring well in the middle of the vale that was used by the whole Barony for miles around. But this tyrant had a strong wall built around it so that none could take any of the water. One bright dawn a rising flood in his grand mansion woke him up. To make a long story short, the evil landlord and all his retinue were drowned before they could escape.

"Fairies are in the old forts," Kelly informed me, "and they take children away. Long ago, before my time, they stole a young colleen from our village, but she managed to escape. She had galore wonderful stories about her adventures and the grand mansion under the Loch."

Myself was cycling home from the town of Elphin one night when a force of peelers halted me.

"What are you doing out at this time?" demanded a burly constable.

"Why can't I be out as well as yourselves?" I replied in the Gaelic, coming down off my bicycle.

That was enough. They arrested me, and when they found no seditious papers on me, they had to be satisfied to take the few pounds in my pockets.

Since the British Government had proclaimed the Gaelic language illegal, I was often arrested and taken to the French Park barrack where myself was searched and beaten, my bicycle broken and my pockets emptied. Then, they would kick me out and force me to walk home.

Most of the clergy were on the side of the people, against the British, and in favor of the Gaelic language. Father Roddy, who was a fluent speaker of the old tongue, gave me a hand when I was teaching in Roscommon. His Reverence, who was a true Gael, asked me one day to find a suit of homespuns for him. So I sent for it to my home in Conamara. When he had on the gray trousers, vest and flannel bawneen, he looked indeed like a well-built Islandman.

When I taught Gaelic in Balltinglass, County Wicklow Barony, I was refused the school by the Bishop of Dunlavin. That pillar of the church was very pro-British, though the Irish Free State was now founded. I tried hard to meet him and have a talk about the Gaelic night school. But I found out that he was high up in the nobility and would not stoop so low as to meet with a Gaelic teacher.

Nevertheless, I got along fine with the classes in the Dunlavin area. We cleaned up an old barn, borrowed stools from the neighbors, and with light from an oil lamp hung on the wall, we carried on nicely all winter.

Myself had found the going hard in the County Wicklow. I had to cycle seven miles out in the country from my lodging house in the town of Balltinglass. Many is the cold winter's night I came to the school drenched to the skin. Often I needs must take off my boots and squeeze the water out of my stockings before entering the classroom.

Cycling through the Glen of Imaal on moonlit nights was a pleasure. Often I met tribes of gypsies and tinkers. Carts loaded with pots, cans and children, drawn by mules and horses. Donkeys and scores of dogs followed the slow-moving caravan. It is a historical fact that the Moffet Clan of tinkers held the mastery east of the Shannon for ages. The small tribes had to pay tithes to lanky side-whiskered Moffet to be allowed to pitch their tents in certain areas.

One evening I was on my way to the town of Balltinglass to teach a class. On reaching the bridge the wonder of the world came on me to see a great crowd of people. Arrah, the two most powerful factions of tinkers with their carts and animals were camped on opposite sides of the bridge. The Ward army, which now had pitched its tents on the bank of the river outside the town, had traveled the long dreary road from Connacht in the west. They had long held the mastery west of the Shannon and were now making a bold bid for the Moffet territory in the east.

Big Tom Ward as he led his men across the country had gained strength galore, for he promised the little tribes that he would free every one of them from the Moffet tithes. Tom and his allies took the precaution to shorten the road by night and rest in the woods by day. Nevertheless, the enemy in some mysterious way had found out that the Wards were coming and had fortified themselves behind the bridge to hold the town.

"Tom Ward has made a bold attempt already. Here he comes again. Arrah, he has a neck like a bull," exclaimed a pudgy little man who sat on the wall looking on.

Four horses, three mules and ten donkeys tried to cross the bridge. The mounted warriors egged on the animals with blackthorn sticks. Dogs and men brought up the rear. But the Moffet forces were on the alert. They rode their animals from behind the barricades, and the two rival forces clashed in the middle of the bridge.

Stalwart Tom himself rode a white steed, his long red beard flowing in the wind as he slashed right and left with two shillelaghs. The Moffet women threw scissors and arrows made out of knitting pins at the giant leader, but they only tickled Big Tom. Some of the weapons were sticking out of his body like the quills of a porcupine.

A scrawny Moffet cavalier who rode a black jennet advanced boldly, raised a tin instrument to his mouth and took such a loud weird screech out of it that the Ward donkeys, terror-stricken, threw their riders and fled in disorder over to the enemy's side. One had the half of his ear chewed off by a Moffet mule. The Wards were forced to retreat with heavy losses. The Moffets, overjoyed with the first flush of victory, sent their women uptown for food and refreshments to celebrate.

But Tom Ward was the kind of man who never gave up. There was a cloud of gloom hanging over the camp now while they had some nourishment. The high-ranking officers, without book or map, discussed their plans for the next maneuver. A large yellow dog, the leader's pet, would not taste a bit of food but strolled down to the river and jumped in as if to get away from it all.

"Come back here, Silvia," Tom called. As the dog returned, wagging her tail, Tom exclaimed, slapping a lieutenant on the back, "Ah, I have it, and I got the idea right now from Silvia. Come along, men."

Big Tom mustered a division of his seasoned troops and maneuvered quietly down behind the old mills on the river bank. Pleasure boats belonging to the nobility of the town were tied up in a cove there, but the oars were locked to the thwarts. The emergency man opened his budget, took out the tinsmith tools and cut the chains. General Tom, with a catlike tread, paced back and forth while he spoke a few words to his troops.

"Men, ye are going into action now and I hope every one of ye will do his duty and be a credit to Connacht. Man the boats!"

The boats began to cross and recross the Slaney; rags laid in the oar beds silenced the oars. Horses, mules and donkeys swam across, the dogs at their tails keeping them in line. Now the Ward home guard composed of pretty colleens started to skirmish and act on the bridge. They crooned lullabies, danced and performed graceful somersaults in scanty tights to keep the enemy entertained and diverted from the main offensive.

The animals got out of the water in regular order and shook themselves. The Ward lieutenants mounted and marched up from the landing place through narrow crooked streets. Arrah, the enemy was taken entirely by surprise when gallant Tom raised his war cry, which was taken up by every man and dog in the ranks as they charged forward.

The Moffet forces, who had been busy making preparations for the grand celebration of their victory, had no choice but to surrender. The Clan Ward flag was raised amid the cheers of the spectators.

"My soul from the devil, but it was a clever bit of strategy," exclaimed a tall slim man who leaned on the wall next to me.

"Indeed, it is a great general or admiral that Big Tom should be, for the ordinary affairs of everyday life have not enough excitement for him," added a stocky short man, wearing a slouched old caubeen set at a rakish angle on his head.

"Musha, what good are all the boasts of the Moffets now, themselves and their blue-blood society kin in America?" asked a gray-haired old man with twinkling dark eyes.

"Big Tom has taught them a thing or two spearheading their positions in Moffet's own bailiwick," put in a hunchback who sat on the highest part of the wall dangling his feet.

While the peace treaty was being discussed, General Ward noticed that the ear of a gray donkey prisoner was chewed off, and this incident deadlocked the conference.

"Foul play," shouted Big Tom. "A prisoner is a prisoner, and, by all the rules of modern warfare, he should be protected on enemy ground instead of being mutilated in cold blood."

"Damn it," retorted one of the Moffet leaders who was tipsy galore. "It was the black mule who done it because your jackass got fresh like his master."

"Fresh or stale," roared Tom, "I'll damn you," knocking him on the rod of his back with the shillelagh.

Scissors, knitting pins and tin arrows began to fly again as Big Tom slashed right and left through his own section of the battlefield. He was going through the enemy like a hawk through a flock of sparrows, and his followers too were laying the Moffet warriors low whenever they came up to them.

The rumble of lorries was heard in the distance.

"Military and peelers!" shouted the spectators.

The peace conference was in full swing again when the police and soldiers arrived.

"Ye are all under arrest for being disturbers of the peace," shouted the commanding officer.

"Well now, but that is strange," spoke Tom in his most polite manner, "for we are the peacemakers and glory be to God on——"

But he was thrown into a lorry on the top of his head by four husky soldiers before he had time to finish. Lanky Moffet with the side whiskers was grabbed by a constable and pitched in on top of him. When all the high-ranking officers were loaded in the trucks, the animals were rounded up and driven to the pound. All the luxuries, whiskey, porter and wine were stowed carefully in a special motor-car and taken to the barrack.

While the prisoners were being questioned and searched, one of the peelers found the half leg of a scissor sticking out of Tom's back, and on opening his vest to pull it out he exclaimed, "My soul from the devil, but he has a sheathing of bright tin around his body for protection."

Later on in the night, while the two rival factions were

snoring in their cells, the soldiers and peelers had a jolly good time drinking the liquor intended for the victory celebration, first by pale-faced Moffet and then again by his rival, Big Tom.

*

When the night school ended in June, I got word from my home in Conamara that the Free State soldiers were looking for me, claiming that I was an organizer of cattle drives. Most of the leaders were already in prisons or concentration camps: Daida, my brother Sean, Colm Connolly, Seamus Cloherty and Luke Nee were with thousands of others. My sister Barbara sent me word that it would not be wise for me to go back home, where I would either be killed or imprisoned by gangs of drunken Free Staters who were now being wined and dined by landlords, the same as the English Black and Tans had been a few years before. So I took to the road.

I soon tired of the bad lodgings, wicked dogs and insects. Nor did I ever meet that colleen the neighbors said would lure me away from my home in the west. Now I agreed with the old Islander in Muighinis who would say that the end of an old gelding, the end of an old sailor, and the end of an old schoolteacher were the worst ends of all.

One night, tired and hungry, I came upon a gypsy's camp at the side of the road. I strolled over to it. "Have you any matches on you?" I asked a tall middle-aged man, though I had neither pipe nor cigarettes.

"Come over here to the fire and put a red on it."

I began to search my pockets. "The devil take it, but I have lost my pipe."

"Here, take a pull out of this dudeen."

"Thank you, a chara."

I took only a few draws. A red-haired woman turned

from her cooking to size up the stranger. Then she gave me a warm ready smile. "He who has his foot on the road needs must be hungry," handing me a mug of tea and a slice of bread.

The two dogs that had barked at me before were watching me closely as I ate. The red-haired raggedy children came closer. While I felt the hot breath of one on the back of my neck, the hand of another stole into my empty pocket, and a little girl started to count the nails in my boots and pick the dirt caked between with her fingers.

"Have you not an easy time spinning around on your wheel," said the woman, handing me a quarter of a rabbit.

"The comfort is no greater than the hardship, my good woman."

"I am a gypsy myself and know no other kind of life," said she.

"You don't say so! It's a free kind of life with few regulations, is it not?"

"Be that as it may, I fell in love with Tom and I only a slip of a girl. Arrah, he swept me off my feet and left me dangling in mid-air. My own tribe was against it—a tinker was no match for a gypsy."

"True love won out," said I.

"We went through the lawful ceremony of Tom's tribe and finished by jumping over the budget hand-in-hand at the Galway races in August."

"I am from Galway myself."

"Indeed, I often sang ballads in the streets there."

"Come over here, Tameen," called the tinker. "Run along now," handing the little one a tin can and putting a whisper in his ear.

The boy was back in a few minutes with the can full of Guinness's porter.

"Bring over the mugs, Maire," Tom ordered, dipping a vessel in the yellow froth and handing it to me. He took another himself, toasting, "Slainte."

An old woman put her head out of a tent and asked for a mouthful to relieve a toothache.

When it was growing dark, the tinker covered the cans he had made during the day with burlap bags lest the dew rust them. Only for the croaking of the frogs in the pond nearby and the flapping of the woman's petticoat fanning the fire, all was silent and peaceful.

"You had better stay here," said she, as she made the tea. "You could sleep with Tom. Though we haven't got a mouthful for the morrow, God help us."

"God helps those who help themselves!" her husband answered. Then turning around, "Would you find any fault to come along for a hunt?"

"All right," I replied, though I was in the dark yet.

He took a coarse bag out of the tent, saying, "Follow me, a chara."

"God save ye from all harm," prayed Maire, handing him a lantern.

I stumbled along after the leader through small gardens choked with briars, furze and stones. As we drew near a farmer's house on the cheek of a hill, he took the red muffler from his neck and wound it around the lantern.

"Wait a minute now until your eyes grow accustomed to the dark. I have had this place on my mind since morning when I did a job of work there. The henhouse is over by the haggard wall. Stay here, you, and, if you notice anything, whistle."

He climbed the stone wall saying some prayers in a low tone. The sleeping village lay on a slope over a glen. Now the landscape was lost in shadows, and a dust of silvery stars were sprinkled in the dome of heaven. Once when a twig snapped under my foot, my heart jumped. Soon I heard him returning.

"Hurry now," he whispered.

Tom was prodding the nature of the ground before us with a blackthorn stick, and, on crossing a field, we ran into a pit of potatoes covered with ferns.

"Hold the bag, no matter about the hens," he ordered, clearing the ferns away and half-filling the bag. Then he stripped the lantern so that we could see our way.

"Only I grabbed the rooster, I could have a few more hens. The devil screeched and when I set him free, the sharp spur on his heel cut my finger. If you carry the bag now, it will help.

"Careful, a chara, your load is heavy and——"

He had not finished before I fell into a drain: "Help! Help!" I shouted, grabbing the bank with my free hand.

"You'll be all right, but the poor hens are drowned," he chuckled, after helping me out. "I should have held the light back for you."

"My boots are full of water and look at my only trousers," moaned I, shaking a shower out of my clothes.

As we drew near the camp, the dogs ran up to us wagging their tails.

"Take off those wet trousers and spread them on the grass, and they will be dry in the morning," Tom ordered, entering the tent.

I slept soundly that night until the clatter of pots and pans woke me at break of day.

"Is there any drop at all in the can?" asked himself, putting his head out of the tent door.

"You know there is not," replied Maire.

"Wake up Tameen, then."

Tameen got up in a hurry, took the can and ran along, the vessel making a tinny sound against his legs.

It was a grand morning, a clear blue sky overhead and the birds singing in the trees that arched the river. Maire threw three of the hens into a pot of boiling water that hung over the fire. A layer of potatoes was laid under the embers and ashes to roast. Mickileen was watching the pot and keeping Seaneen, Maireen and Phegeen back from the fire. The whistling of Tameen was heard coming back with the drink.

"Is there any drying at all on my trousers?" I asked, with my head out between the tent flaps.

"It is as wet as the dung yet," replied Tom, "for there was a heavy dew last night."

"Would you have a spare to lend me?"

"No, Tameen cut the legs of the old one so that it would fit him."

"Put on this petticoat," said Maire, pitching it in.

"My soul from the devil, but yourself would make the pretty girl with golden curls and rosy cheeks," laughed Tom, blowing the foam off a mug of porter.

"Come over here, colleen bhan, and have a mouthful," Maire invited, with a hearty free laugh.

A coarse bag lay on the grass with a mountain of roasted potatoes in the center and the cooked hens at the base. The dogs started to growl, eyeing me in the red petticoat. The tinker shook his fist at them and told them to behave for their own good.

"I'll place the can right here in the center of the parish," he smiled, digging a place in the potatoes. He handed me a mug of porter. The children came around with their tin mugeens for their share of drink. Mickileen tossed back his behind Tom's back, came around again and got another ration. Tameen tried the same trick, but Tom grew angry, saying, "Ye bold little schemers, and it is not from myself ye took it."

Breakfast over, we stretched on the green and started telling old stories. Tom's finger was paining him, and he sent Tameen to a neighbor's barn for a spider's web and moldy moss to apply to the cut. The old woman who was confined to her bed with her first toothache was ninety years of age.

Tom handed me the pipe, and I was ashamed to refuse. I smoked and talked, but a bad taste came into my mouth and the place seemed to be spinning around.

"I want to see if my trousers are dry," I stammered, staggering to my feet. The ground seemed to be heaving like the deck of a boat in a choppy sea.

When I did not return, my host went looking for me. He found me dead to the world and the red petticoat crumpled above my knees.

When I woke up, the yellow dog was sleeping on my trousers, and I had to wake him, too. Tom was stripped to the shirt making cans, and the children had gone into the village begging. I got my bicycle ready and was about to leave when Maire invited me into the tent.

"You might as well have another drop of tea, and it will cure your headache."

"The poor man's labor is never done, a chara, but there is no use complaining. Good-bye and may the road be kind to you." I mounted my old bicycle. And again I was facing the long white roads.

That evening I arrived in the town of Newbridge, County Kildare, where there was work aplenty on the bogs. I found lodging for the night and was up early the next morning and making for the peat bogs. There were hundreds of acres in that barony alone. Workers galore arrived from all parts of Eire.

A ganger came over to me, saluted in a friendly manner and said, "Which would you prefer, cutting or spreading? Did you cut any turf before?"

"I often used the turf spade in Conamara," I replied.

"You have come a long way. We have cutters here from Galway. We pay two pounds a week."

In a short time I met a few of the Galway men. They were staying in Newbridge, so we used to be home together and often went into a pub for a few drinks of Guinness's stout.

The weather was lovely and we liked the work. But on the third day for me, we heard the rumbling of lorries coming down a dirt road in the peat land. What were they looking for?

"Free State soldiers!" was shouted here and there. "Those devils are out for murder. Hurry, hurry and take cover."

We rushed down into the holes where we had cut the turf. They opened fire, peppering the turf banks. It seemed so silly, for we had no arms. Nevertheless, all were taken prisoners and marched to the barrack in Naas, County Kildare, where they searched us.

"Where are you from?" an officer asked myself in a Cockney accent that I found hard to understand.

"From the West," I replied in the Gaelic.

"Do you belong to the Irregulars?" (That's what they called the I.R.A.)

I answered him again in the Gaelic. That was enough. They kicked and cursed me. I saw no more of my bog friends, as we were put in different rooms. Then I was put back in the lorry again, and as luck would have it, brought to the town of Balltinglass, County Wicklow, where my friends and former Gaelic students soon got me out on bail.

I often had heard about Rinn College, County Waterford, and now I made up my mind to go there. The sunbeams danced on the dark river and the breezes swished along, raising flurries of white dust that circled around me. That evening I arrived in Rinn and the Fear Mor, who was president of the college, put a céad míle fáilte before me. The Fear Mor—Big Man—was well-named, for he was over six feet tall, broad-shouldered, with a mop of dark hair. I attended the course and took the examination. It was a most enjoyable and gainful month, for I won a Gaelic Diploma from the famous Rinn College.

The day came at last when I bade good-bye to Rinn and faced the long white roads again. That evening I stopped at the town of Enniscorthy, County Wexford, to have a meal. Whom should I meet then but Seamus Doyle, who was one of the heroes of the Easter Week Rebellion, 1916. He had been sentenced to life imprisonment by an English court-martial, but was released at the time of the General Amnesty. Now Seamus was the organizer of the Wexford Gaelic League.

"Would you like to teach here with us?" he asked me.

"Indeed, I would be very happy."

So I lowered my sails and started the next night teaching Gaelic in the old Rebel Hall of Enniscorthy. I had classes from eight to ten for five nights a week. I conducted two classes in the Presentation Convent and two in the Mercy Convent from four to five in the afternoons. The nuns were happy and willing workers, and it was a pleasure for me to teach them. After the classes there was always tea for me, and on sunshiny days we had both classes and lunch in their lovely gardens. While the classes were being held, they were the perfect students and respected their teacher, but when the work was finished all this was changed. The nuns were like a frolicsome group of children freed from school. They soon learned that their teacher was shy before any woman, even one clothed in the holy habit of the sister. They teased me. One would put red roses in my buttonhole, which was no redder than my cheeks under their merciless banter. Still and all, though relieved to escape from their teasing, I was always happy to return to those gay and innocent colleens.

Word came to me that it would be safe enough to return to my home in the West. Things had quieted down and a sort of armistice prevailed. After completing my teaching in County Wexford, I was offered a position in County Sligo. Seemingly all was going well until I learned that to hold this position, or any other government job, one must sign the Oath of Allegiance to England. This I refused to do, which ended my career as a Gaelic teacher in Eire. It was then that I decided to emigrate, and without waiting any longer I booked passage for Canada on the liner *Athenia*.

✳

Locked in a cranny of my mind is the picture, as clear
and near as if it were today, of that May morning a half-
century ago. My Mama shaking with sobs from the loneliness; my father sitting on a chair, brave enough as usual
to hold back his grief. Both bade me their farewells and
kissed me again and again. Daida handed me forty gold
sovereigns for fear I would need them on the long trip to
the foreign land. I remember that the kitchen window was
a little open from the bottom, and our gray cat sunning
herself and curled around a yellow earthen pot resting on
the sill holding geraniums that my sister Mairin had planted
a few years before. A brown cruiskeen of mountain dew
and a score of glasses stood on the mahogany table. The
white fine sand spread on the floor sparkled, and the delph
on the red dresser glittered from the wavering flames of
the turf fire on the hearth.

Our dog, Watch, seemed to know that something was
not as it should be. He sneaked up close to my side and
jumped up to kiss my face. As we walked on through the
garden to the west, primroses growing by the path waved
their golden heads as the wisps of wind caressed them. A
plump yellow bee lay on a white clover blossom sucking
the honey. Paddy son-of-Colm, a new patch of white
flannel on his elbow, walked before me.

Mickileen son-of-Liam kept close to my side, a shillelagh in his hand, and he starting to tell a story to shorten
the road: Fionn MacCumhal, commander in chief of the
Fianna, was a wise and noble warrior. Yet, his sweetheart,

Grainne, made a big fool out of him when she eloped with
Diarmuid, a plain soldier in the ranks. Mighty Fionn was
mad enough to be tied, but, by chewing on his thumb, he
found out that his bold rival was sleeping on the heather.
The noble leader ordered out a regiment of his well-trained
warriors at once to search the hills and mountains. They
did, but failed to find a single clue of the elopers. He
chewed his magic thumb again—bit it, I should say, for it
had to be cobwebbed and bandaged. But it did show this
time that they were lying on the sand. Fionn now mustered
three special divisions of seasoned troops and ordered them
to comb the strands and shores of Eire to try and catch the
culprits. Once more, it was all in vain.

"Mind you, Grainne was well up to her former lover and
told this fresh lad to bring a sack of heather down from
the mountain to sleep on while at the shore. Again, when
they grew tired of the shore, this husky young fellow carried a heavy bag of fine sand from the strand up to the
hill to sleep on. Poor Fionn was fooled all the way.

"But as time passed, Fionn and his rival became steadfast
friends, dined and feasted each other in turns. Lovely
Grainne herself was the favorite dame in the Banquet Hall
of Fionn's Grand Mansion. Had Fionn's love cooled?

"To be sure, that's the way with the world, Jimeen.
The big empires of this old world were murdering each
other a couple of years ago, and right now are killing
each other with kindness and kisses."

Luke son-of-Paudeen, Seaneen son-of-Mickil, and Martin
son-of-Anna shook my hands. The Rover slapped me on
the back and advised me to be careful in the new land.
O'Cooney grinned, bade me to drink his health and have
a jolly time with the women. I kissed Mama and Daida and

my sisters and brothers and said goodbye to every one of the neighbors for the last time.

As the jaunting car that was taking me to the railroad station at Recess rounded the first curve in the path of my new life, I got the last glimpse of the friends of my heart with their hands raised waving their handkerchiefs and caubeens. Driving by out on the mainland, galore of the villagers with their turf spades on their shoulders were walking along the road going to the bogs to cut the turf. I envied them their minds at ease without a notion of leaving their native land.

That was many years ago and water galore has run since and generations of grass have grown. To those who have found death—Daida, the storytellers, fishermen, colleens, kind-hearted women and all my old friends—may the blessing of dear God be with them, gone with the tide to some other shore. Young and old, they will always remain to me as I knew them then until myself too will have gone with the ebb.